DATE DUE

FEB -2 2001			
	MAY 0 4 2002		

Demco

ENTRANCES AND EXITS

Entrances and Exits

A BOOK OF PLAYS FOR YOUNG ACTORS

Selected by Phyllis Fenner and Avah Hughes

Illustrated by Frank Kramer

DODD, MEAD & COMPANY   NEW YORK

Library of Congress Catalog Card Number: 60-11919

Printed in the United States of America

by Vail-Ballou Press, Inc., Binghamton, N. Y.

"It is the supreme art of the teacher
to awaken joy in creative expression . . ." *

TO OUR FRIEND, LU WRIGHT,
WHO HAS THAT ART

* Albert Einstein

CONTENTS

King John and the Abbot
of Canterbury

A PLAY IN FOUR SCENES BASED ON THE OLD LEGEND

BY RUTH VICKERY HOLMES

Characters

SHEPHERD

KING JOHN

FIRST NOBLEMAN

SECOND NOBLEMAN

ABBOT OF CANTERBURY

REGENT OF CAMBRIDGE

REGENT OF OXFORD

KING JOHN AND THE ABBOT OF CANTERBURY
Reprinted from *Plays,* The Drama Magazine for Young People, 8 Arlington St., Boston 16, Mass. Copyright © 1941 by Plays, Inc.

KING JOHN AND THE ABBOT OF CANTERBURY

King John and the Abbot of Canterbury is a play based on an old English ballad. It is an amusing and comic folk-tale plot of trial by question in which a bright person substitutes for a stupid one.

King John of England was the youngest brother of Richard, the Lion Hearted, who fought in the second Crusade against the Mohammedans. Richard was loved and respected by all of his subjects, even his enemies. After Richard's death, John became King of England.

The longer John ruled, the more cruel he became. He taxed and oppressed his people until they could no longer endure his wickedness. Some of his noblemen took him prisoner and sent him to the island of Runnymede. Here they forced him to sign an agreement to give his people more privileges and freedom. This agreement was called the Magna Charta.

All Kings of England who succeeded him had to agree to the items which John had signed.

This play, *King John and the Abbot of Canterbury,* shows how John planned to seize property which did not belong to him and how he treated some of the good people in his kingdom.

Scene I

A country roadside. Tall hedges across rear, and low bushes with clumps of grass to give desired effect.

AT RISE [SHEPHERD *enters from left center, talking to his sheep offstage behind him.*]

SHEPHERD [*Without looking back*]: Come on now. If you stop to nibble at every green sprout on the road, I'll never reach the Abbey by nightfall. [KING JOHN *enters behind the* SHEPHERD, *and unnoticed by him.*]

[*Emphatically to his sheep, without looking behind him, but swinging his crook dangerously near* KING JOHN.]

Get on with you, I say. Or else you'll feel the prodding of my crook.

KING JOHN [*Sharply*]: Are those words meant for me, Sirrah?

SHEPHERD [*Turning toward* KING JOHN, *astonished at his presence there*]: What? The King? [*Bowing low.*] Your Majesty's pardon. I thought the sheep and I had the road to ourselves. I was but urging them to move faster. [FIRST *and* SECOND NOBLEMEN *enter, and stand respectfully behind the* KING.]

KING JOHN [*Turning to* FIRST NOBLEMAN. *In a sneering tone*]: This varlet here wants the road to himself. He even suggests prodding his King with his sword.

SHEPHERD [*Protesting*]: Indeed, your Majesty—I did not mean—I did not know—

KING JOHN [*Interrupting*]: I go for a stroll while the horses rest. And a country oaf orders me to *get on*. He threatens to *prod me*. [*Turning toward* SECOND NOBLEMAN.] What think you he deserves?

SECOND NOBLEMAN [*Stepping toward* SHEPHERD]: Shall I run my blade through his heart?

FIRST NOBLEMAN [*Drawing close to* KING]: Or does your Majesty wish him saved for hanging?

SHEPHERD [*Stepping backward*]: Your Majesty, I entreat you to hear me. I was but trying to hurry my sheep. I promised to get them to the Abbey e're nightfall. The Abbot says that no sheep near Canterbury are so tender as mine.

KING JOHN [*Pacing back and forth in anger*]: Ha! So your sheep are for the Abbot of Canterbury. Worse and worse. The tales that have been brought me of his arrogance!

SECOND NOBLEMAN [*Nodding*]: His wealth is at fault. Such gold as flows from his hands results naturally in arrogance and pride.

FIRST NOBLEMAN [*Going close to* KING]: Yes. 'Tis the common report that a full hundred nobles feast with him each night.

KING JOHN [*Angrily*]: He keeps court in grand style. With more lavish spending than his King contrives.

FIRST NOBLEMAN [*Nodding agreement*]: Should any man in the land live better than the King?

KING JOHN [*Vigorously*]: That no man shall do. The Abbot flies high. But I will trim his wings. [*Pauses to think, then steps toward* SHEPHERD.] To you I will be lenient. I will spare your life. Be off with you now. And say to the Abbot of Canterbury that he is summoned to our presence. Let him reach the court in three days' time.

SHEPHERD [*Bowing*]: My thanks, your Majesty. [*Stepping forward sturdily.*] But the Abbot. It was no fault of his, your Majesty, that my sheep blocked your Majesty's road.

KING JOHN [*With wrath*]: Hold your tongue, man. Our business with the Abbot is in no way your concern. But your life, and his as well, will be the forfeit should he fail to reach our court in three days' time.

Curtain

Scene II

Throne room in KING JOHN'S *palace. Appropriate lavish furnishings, with throne in a conspicuous position, placed obliquely to the audience.*

KING JOHN [*To* FIRST NOBLEMAN]: So the Abbot has

arrived, and waits to be received. Well, show him in.

FIRST NOBLEMAN [*Bowing*]: As your Majesty wishes. [*Goes out.*]

SECOND NOBLEMAN [*Turning toward* KING]: I'll wager that the trip to court was none to his liking. The hardships of the road would not be easy for one used to the comforts of Canterbury.

KING JOHN [*Nodding*]: The comforts—humph—the luxury. Well, the Abbot may find that other details of this journey are none too much to his liking. [FIRST NOBLEMAN *enters, followed by the* ABBOT, *who bows low.*] Ah, so you're here, my good Abbot.

ABBOT [*Bowing again*]: At your service, your Majesty. As a loyal subject, I hastened to obey your summons.

KING JOHN [*Sneering*]: As a *loyal* subject? Does a *loyal* subject live in such state that his daily banquets outdo in grandeur those at the court of his king?

ABBOT [*Stepping nearer to the throne*]: O King, I do not know what the reports are that may have reached your ears, but I attempt no grandeur. I simply try to make life pleasant for my friends.

KING JOHN [*Sternly*]: And you pour out gold with lavish hand in doing it.

ABBOT [*Firmly*]: I provide only what I can well afford. I spend nothing but what is my own.

KING JOHN [*Leaning forward*]: Then you have greater riches than your king. Should a loyal subject live better than his king? No, I say. No man in the land shall live better than the king.

ABBOT [*Drawing back*]: I pray your Majesty to think no ill of a subject who had no wrong intent.

KING JOHN [*In anger*]: Think no ill of a subject who puts his king to shame by living in grandeur greater than the royal court's? Perhaps you think that's suitable. No doubt you think that the Abbot of Canterbury is greater than the King of

England.

ABBOT [*Emphatically*]: Oh, no, your Majesty. No.

KING JOHN [*Interrupting with mounting anger*]: Not another word. Your fault is plain. For such disloyalty your head should be cut off, and all your riches become mine.

ABBOT [*Advancing toward the throne*]: But, your Majesty, I do protest my innocence of evil intent. I crave your leniency.

KING JOHN [*Haughtily*]: Your fault is plain, I say. You have assumed the right of royal grandeur. You are guilty of a grave offense. And yet you crave my leniency.

ABBOT [*Bowing*]: As a subject whose every thought is loyal to his king, I crave your leniency and pardon.

SECOND NOBLEMAN [*Going close to* KING]: Pardon, your Majesty, but may I suggest—

KING JOHN [*Nodding to* FIRST NOBLEMAN, *then turning toward* ABBOT]: I shall take a moment to reflect. That I am always fair and just is known to all. I will consider carefully before I make my sentence final. [ABBOT *turns, and goes slowly toward left, where he turns and stands with bowed head.* KING JOHN *and the two* NOBLEMEN *whisper together.*]

FIRST NOBLEMAN [*Audibly*]: You see . . . Your Majesty's best interests would not be affected. But your generosity would be made plain.

KING JOHN [*Nodding, then leaning forward toward the* ABBOT]: You ask that I be lenient, and grant pardon.

ABBOT [*Drawing close to* KING]: I do, O King.

KING JOHN [*Pleasantly*]: Then I will, this time, be lenient.

ABBOT [*Fervently*]: My humble thanks, your Majesty. My gratitude—

KING JOHN [*Interrupting*]: But, naturally, upon certain conditions.

ABBOT [*Taken aback*]: Upon certain conditions?

KING JOHN [*Nodding*]: Naturally, so grave an offense cannot be pardoned outright. But the conditions are generous. You have only to answer three questions. Then your life will be spared, and your estate remain yours.

ABBOT [*Warily*]: May I ask what the questions are, your Majesty? Gladly I'll answer your questions.

KING JOHN [*With solemnity*]: Well, then. Here's the first question: As I sit here with my crown of gold on my head, you must tell me to within a day just how long I shall live.

ABBOT [*Protesting*]: But, your Majesty—

KING JOHN [*Firmly*]: Next, you must tell me how soon I shall ride round the whole world.

ABBOT [*Shrugging his shoulders*]: But your Majesty knows that no man could answer—

KING JOHN [*Interrupting*]: And, lastly you shall tell me what I think.

ABBOT [*Distressed*]: Is it in human power to read the mind of another? [*Pauses, bowing his head in thought, then looks up slowly.*] If the answering of these questions is beyond my power, what then?

KING JOHN [*Nodding*]: Then, naturally, the forfeit must be paid—your life and your riches.

ABBOT [*Despondent*]: Ah, your Majesty, I see—I see what you mean.

KING JOHN [*With sternness*]: Do you, or do you not, accept the condition?

ABBOT [*Gathering courage*]: I accept, your Majesty. But to one so generous in his leniency, I make this request. To questions so profound, to questions that concern your Majesty's own person, it would not be in order to give unstudied answers. I beg for two weeks' time. Then I'll return, and give such answers as I can.

KING JOHN [*Turning to* SECOND NOBLEMAN]: Would such delay be overmuch, do you think? Shall we grant the Abbot two weeks' time?

FIRST NOBLEMAN [*Bowing*]: Two weeks will not, I think, affect the outcome to his Majesty's disfavor. Let the Abbot have his two weeks.

KING JOHN [*To* ABBOT]: It is our pleasure to answer favorably. Your request is granted. In two weeks' time, return and give the answers. Fail not to be present here in two weeks' time.

Curtain

Scene III

A room in the Abbey. Furnished simply with a table surrounded by chairs.

AT RISE [THE ABBOT *is seated behind the table,* THE REGENT OF CAMBRIDGE *at the right end of the table, and* THE REGENT OF OXFORD, *at the left end.*]

ABBOT [*Sighing*]: Then in all Cambridge, no help could be found?

REGENT OF CAMBRIDGE [*Nodding*]: No answers to such questions as the King's are possible, my lord. Our most noted scholars all agree to that.

ABBOT [*Turning to* THE REGENT OF OXFORD]: And your report, too, is the same? Was there no one at Oxford who could solve them?

REGENT OF OXFORD [*Gravely*]: Indeed, my lord, we scholars of Oxford are in agreement. The questions put to you by the King *cannot* be answered.

ABBOT [*Despondent*]: That, I acknowledge, is doubtless his intent. The questions are unanswerable. When I start back to court tomorrow, no hope goes with me. I fear my life has nearly run its course.

SHEPHERD [*Entering from right, and bowing*]: Your pardon, my lord. You have helped me these long years past. Now I've come to help you. I beg leave to take your trouble from your back, and bear it on my own.

ABBOT [*Looking up, surprised*]: Those are brave words. But have you knowledge of what confronts me?

SHEPHERD [*Nodding*]: Ay, my lord, I know full well. I know the condition made by the King for your pardon. It is a sentence of death, in a manner of speaking. But I know, too, how to save you. Let the whole matter be simply a jest. . . .

ABBOT [*Drawing himself up, annoyed*]: Your concern, if concern it is, makes your words sound like a fool's.

SHEPHERD [*Stepping nearer*]: But, my lord, have you never heard that a fool may teach a wise man wit? Have all the scholars of Cambridge and of Oxford, or your own scholars here in Canterbury, met with success? What help has come from them?

REGENT OF CAMBRIDGE [*Interrupting*]: None, by my faith. No help at all.

SHEPHERD [*Turning, and nodding*]: The good sir bears me out. The questions put you by the King were naught but jests, most cruel jests. Well, then. As fire puts out fire, so meet jest with jest.

ABBOT [*Nodding*]: Go on. Wisdom, perhaps, is the real root of what I took for folly. Tell me what you have planned.

SHEPHERD [*Leaning on the table*]: Lend me your horse and gown, and servants to go with me. A false beard, too, must be on my chin. Then I, as the Abbot of Canterbury, will keep the tryst in London.

ABBOT [*Surprised*]: Where, as Abbot of Canterbury, you are likely to die. A good friend you are to call that a jest.

SHEPHERD [*Firmly*]: And is my life of such account as yours? But there are other jests I've thought of. The answers to the questions. There is a chance—such jests as mine, perchance might win the day.

REGENT OF OXFORD [*Nodding to* ABBOT]: If the fellow's wit matches the stoutness of his heart, the day may yet be saved. I'll ride in his train to see his courage put to action.

REGENT OF CAMBRIDGE [*Agreeing*]: And so will I. And I pray Heaven that all goes well.

SHEPHERD [*Bows to express his thanks, then faces* ABBOT]: But if worst comes to worst, I will die in your place.

ABBOT [*With decision*]: No. That you'll not. I, too, will ride in your train, concealed in your cloak and hood. But if worst comes to worst, I will die for myself.

Curtain

Scene IV

Same as Scene II.

AT RISE [KING JOHN *on throne.* FIRST NOBLEMAN, SECOND NOBLEMAN, *behind center.* SHEPHERD, *disguised as* ABBOT, *stands facing* KING JOHN.]

KING JOHN [*Sneering*]: Welcome, Sir Abbot, welcome. Just two weeks to the day since your last visit. [SHEPHERD *bows.*]

FIRST NOBLEMAN [*With sarcasm*]: The Abbot has, no doubt, spent the full two weeks studying His Majesty's questions.

SHEPHERD [*Bowing*]: Ay. With most careful consideration.

SECOND NOBLEMAN [*With derision*]: And, no doubt, with his careful consideration, the Abbot has found answers to all the questions.

SHEPHERD [*Bowing*]: Ay. Answers to all the three questions.

KING JOHN [*Nettled*]: Indeed. Indeed. And you know that failure to answer will cost you your life? You must ask no more leniency of me. A bargain's a bargain, and should be kept fair and square. All the world may bear witness that I'm always fair.

SHEPHERD [*Bowing*]: Thank you, your Majesty, for so proper a suggestion.

KING JOHN [*Astonished*]: Suggestion? What suggestion did I make?

SHEPHERD [*Bowing*]: But we need hardly call on all the world to bear witness in this case. Sufficient it will be to have present the three friends who came with me. May they be summoned here, your Majesty?

KING JOHN [*In anger*]: What, sir? Did you bring witnesses?

FIRST NOBLEMAN [*Drawing close to* KING]: Your Majesty's title to the Abbey will be the better established. And the justice of the sentence more plainly proved.

KING JOHN [*Dubiously*]: True. Entirely true. Let the Abbot's friends be summoned. [FIRST NOBLEMAN *goes out left second.*] [*Nodding.*] Your three friends—all the world—it matters not to me who bears witness.

FIRST NOBLEMAN [*Entering from left, followed by* THE REGENT OF CAMBRIDGE, THE REGENT OF OXFORD, *and* THE ABBOT, *disguised in* SHEPHERD'S *cloak and hood*]: Your Majesty, the Regent of Cambridge. [*Who bows.*] The Regent of Oxford. [*Who bows.*] And the simple Shepherd you once saw before. [*Who bows.*]

KING JOHN [*Leaning forward*]: Ah ha, the Shepherd. Well, no more ado. Our business must proceed. Now, then, Sir Abbot, it is understood. If you fail to answer my three questions, you shall lose your head, and your wealth shall be mine.

SHEPHERD [*Nodding assent*]: And if, your Majesty, I give you answers, then my life is to be spared, and my estate remain my own.

KING JOHN [*Turning to look at the witnesses*]: Yes, that is the bargain as it stands. [*To* SHEPHERD.] Now, then, the questions. Tell me, Sir Abbot, to the day, *How Long Shall I Live?*

SHEPHERD [*Slowly, with great solemnity*]: You shall live until the day that you die, and not one day longer. And you shall die when you take your last breath, and not one moment before.

KING JOHN [*Baffled and uncertain*]: You are witty, indeed. But we will let that pass, and say that your answer is right. And now tell me this: *How Soon May I Ride Round the Whole World?*

SHEPHERD [*Profoundly*]: You must rise with the sun, and you must ride with the sun until it rises again the next morning. As soon as you do that, you will find that you have ridden round the whole world in twenty-four hours.

KING JOHN [*Smiling with reluctance*]: Indeed, Sir Abbot, you are not only witty, you are wise. I had not myself thought that so long a journey could take so little time. [*Then leaning forward, sternly.*] But enough. As you value your life, no more jesting. Tell me this if you can. *What Do I Think?*

SHEPHERD [*Pauses, as if lost in thought; then stepping forward*]: You *think*, your Majesty, you *think*—that I am the Abbot of Canterbury.

KING JOHN [*In triumph*]: Ha, I *know* it. Knowing is not the same as thinking. You've not told me what I *think*.

SHEPHERD [*Interrupting*]: But, your Majesty, look. [*Throws off gown and pulls the beard away.*] Not the Abbot am I. But only his shepherd. [KING JOHN *laughs in spite of himself, then laughs more loudly, and all present join in.*] [*Stepping nearer the throne.*] Forgive me, your Majesty. I came in the hope that the Abbot would be saved. A bargain's a bargain.

KING [*Breaking in*]: Which I'll keep fair and square as all can bear witness. Your wit has served both you and the Abbot. Four pieces of silver each week shall be yours your life long.

SHEPHERD [*Bowing*]: My thanks, your Majesty. But the Abbot? Do you pardon the Abbot?

KING [*Turns and looks at the witnesses; then turns to look at each* NOBLEMAN; *then nods slowly*]: For the Abbot, a free pardon from the King.

    Curtain

PRODUCTION NOTES

Characters: 7 male; may be additional court attendants for Scene 4.

Playing time: 20 minutes

Costumes: Shepherd is dressed in close-fitting brown trousers fastened to the knee with hempen cord; tan tunic; long brown hooded cloak. King John wears tunic of gold cloth, crimson hose, a long crimson cape, and a gold crown. The First Nobleman wears a tunic of figured brocade, a short green cape, green hose. He carries a sword at his side. The Second Nobleman wears a silver tunic, tan velvet cape, tan hose, and carries a sword at his side. The Abbot has a beard and wears purple robes trimmed with white fur. The Regents wear black velvet robes over their gowns of different shades—one light blue and one yellow.

Properties: A heavy walking stick representing shepherd's crook.

Setting: For Scene 1, there is a tall hedge across the rear with low bushes along the side, to give effect of country roadside. Scene 2 may be made to look lavish with large throne decorated with gold (gold paint may be used), and draped with dark purple velvet or anything else to suggest sumptuous furnishings. Scene 3 requires only a table and a few chairs. Scene 4 is the same as Scene 2.

Lighting: No special effects.

Polly Patchwork

BY RACHEL FIELD

Characters

POLLY
THE GRANDMOTHER
GREAT-AUNT MEHITABEL ⎫
GENERAL LAFAYETTE ⎬ *people in dream*
COUSIN MARIANA GAY ⎭
MR. TIPPET
THE SCHOOL MISTRESS
MARY JANE PETERS
JIMMY WILLIS
SCHOLARS, VISITORS, MOTHERS, ETC.

POLLY PATCHWORK

Polly Patchwork comes from *Polly Patchwork Plays,* the popular little book written and illustrated by Rachel Field.

This is a play with an early American background. It centers around a spelling match in a colonial school. Polly's dress, made by her grandmother from a patchwork quilt, helped her win the spelling match and the medal.

Rachel Field interpreted the early American scene with sensitivity and beauty. Her writings are true expressions of children's thoughts and feelings.

Suggestions for costumes, scenery, setting and production of *Polly Patchwork* are incorporated in the script.

Scene I

The interior of a cottage. If possible, there should be a window and a door and a fireplace. There should be a table and at least two chairs, one a small rocker for the GRAND-MOTHER; *an old chest in one corner, plates and china pitcher on shelf or mantelpiece, and a little cot for* POLLY *to sleep on.*

When the curtain rises the GRANDMOTHER *is at the window. She has white hair and a shawl, full skirts and an apron. Of course, spectacles.*

GRANDMOTHER: There! I can hear the geese flying south. There aren't any more marigolds in the garden, and all the berries are falling from the thorn tree. [*Sighs.*] Yes, winter is nearly here, and Polly will need a new dress to keep her warm.

[*She gets down the china pitcher, brings it to the table, empty-ing out the pennies. She sighs again as she counts them and sees how few there are.*]

Dear, dear, not nearly enough to buy Polly a dress, though, to be sure, it doesn't take so many yards to go around her.

[*Enter* POLLY *with a little basket of red berries. She is rather small and wears an old brown dress with several patches in it.*]

POLLY: Oh, Grandmother, may I have a needle and thread?

GRANDMOTHER [*Putting pitcher back*]: What do you want them for, child?

POLLY [*Holding out basket*]: I want to string myself a neck-lace out of these red berries. They look so red and shiny, I'm sure they'll help to keep me warm this winter.

GRANDMOTHER [*Shaking her head as she gets the needle and thread from her basket*]: Red beads are all very fine, but they won't keep the wind out like woollen. [*Giving* POLLY *a threaded needle.*] We must see what we can find in the old chest.

[POLLY *sits down and begins to string her beads. The* GRAND-MOTHER *goes over to the chest, opens it and begins to take out different things: a guitar with faded ribbons and only one string; a very dilapidated high silk hat; a parasol without any handle or with the covering in tatters; a shoe buckle and any other odds and ends that can be thought of; last of all, at the bottom, a brightly colored patchwork quilt, the "crazy quilt" pattern.*]

GRANDMOTHER [*As she takes things out*]: Well, well, if there isn't that old guitar from down South. *That's* no good to us, not even the ribbons. [*She puts aside the guitar.*] And here's your grandfather's best hat. [*She dusts it off, but puts it down, too.*] He used to wear it every Sunday to church at Cranberry Common. [*Putting down the parasol.*] And this will never do to keep out the rain. [*Holding up shoe buckle.*] Too bad the other buckle's lost. It would look queer to see only one on your shoes. [*Handles the other things. Finally holds up quilt.*]

Look, Polly, the very thing! Not a hole in it and we have quilts to sleep under, so this will do nicely for your dress.

POLLY: But, Grandmother, I never saw a dress made out of a quilt before.

GRANDMOTHER [*Turning it this way and that and smiling over the quilt*]: It will keep you as warm as toast, and every patch is real silk.

POLLY: But, Grandmother, whoever—

GRANDMOTHER [*Paying no attention to her*]: Run out now, Polly, and get a basketful of pine cones to start the fire.

POLLY [*Holding up the string of berries*]: Can I put my red beads on now, Grandmother?

GRANDMOTHER [*Already spreading the quilt out on the table and taking up the scissors*]: Yes, child, but hurry and bring the cones in. It's nearly dark.

[POLLY *goes out with her basket. The* GRANDMOTHER *bends over the table with her scissors. She should have her back to the audience, so it will look as if she were really cutting the quilt out. This done, she carries the dress pieces to the rocking chair and begins to sew, rocking and singing all the while.*]

GRANDMOTHER [*Singing*]:

> Fold and snip, and snip and fold,
> Some are young and some are old.
> In and out, and out and in,
> Some will dance and some will spin.
> Sew and stitch, and stitch and sew,
> Some will come and some will go.
> Knot and twist, and twist and knot,
> Some will wed and some will not.

POLLY [*Returning with the cones*]: Here they are, Grandmother. Shall I put them on the fire?

GRANDMOTHER [*Nodding and continuing her song*]:

> Fold and snip, and snip and fold,
> Some are young and some are old, etc., etc.

[POLLY, *in putting cones on, drops some on the floor. She goes over to corner and takes an old-fashioned broom to sweep them up. Her* GRANDMOTHER *sees this and stops singing.*]

Mercy me, child! You mustn't do that! It's past six o'clock, and don't you remember how many times I've told you it brings bad luck to sweep the floor after the sun goes down?

POLLY [*Putting away broom and taking down a primer book from the shelf*]: Then I'll study my spelling lesson, to be all ready for the spelling match.

GRANDMOTHER [*Not looking up from the sewing*]: What's that you said about a spelling match?

POLLY: Oh, Grandmother, they're having one at school on Friday. It's the last day of the fall term.

GRANDMOTHER: I expect all the School Committee will be there to hear you.

POLLY: Yes, and there's a solid-silver medal for the one who wins it. [*A pause.*] I wish I could win it.

GRANDMOTHER: But you're not very good at spelling, are you, Polly?

POLLY [*Rather sadly*]: Not so very . . . [*She is standing by the window, and, as she looks out, she points eagerly.*] Look, there's the little new moon up over the pine tree! [*She shuts her eyes, looks over her left shoulder and whispers something.*] There! I wished on it. I wished that I'd win the spelling match. Do you think it will help me, Grandmother?

GRANDMOTHER [*Sewing away very hard*]: I'm sure I don't know, child.

POLLY [*Going to the other chair and sitting down to study her lesson*]: Well, it can't do any harm to have the moon on my side, can it?

    Curtain

    Scene II

    The cottage just before bedtime. By candlelight. POLLY *is standing up before her* GRANDMOTHER *to have the new dress fitted. It is still not finished, but it is in progress and sticks out stiffly all around* POLLY, *who keeps trying to smooth it down. She does not look as pleased over it as her* GRANDMOTHER, *who snips and fits and pins away happily, talking as she works.*

GRANDMOTHER: Stand very still now while I fit this to you. My, my, it was a mercy I found it in time for the spelling match. I wouldn't want you to stand up before everybody in your old one.

POLLY [*Twisting her head to see back and trying to flatten the skirt again*]: But, Grandmother, it sticks out so—all around me.

GRANDMOTHER: Oh, well, it will flatten down after you've worn it a while. I guess it won't matter if it does balloon out a little, the colors are so nice and bright.

POLLY [*Sighing*]: Yes, they *are* pretty bright.

GRANDMOTHER [*Going on happily, fitting as she talks*]: They call this the crazy-quilt pattern because the pieces are different shapes and sewed together every-which-way. I can remember seeing Great-Aunt Mehitabel making it when I was a little girl no bigger than you. [*Pointing to one of the patches.*] Well, now, if there isn't that patch from the Sea Captain's handkerchief.

POLLY [*Interested in spite of herself*]: Where?

GRANDMOTHER [*Showing her*]: This red one. He gave it to Great-Aunt Mehitabel when she was a little girl. She told me so herself, and how he had a parrot that could whistle "Yankee Doodle" and say, "Trim your sails and face the music." [*The* GRANDMOTHER *should imitate the parrot when she says this.*] And here's the yellow one from the dress she wore the time she danced with General Lafayette.

POLLY [*Showing great surprise*]: Great-Aunt Mehitabel danced?

GRANDMOTHER: I should say she did! She danced the minuet with him, right before the Governor and all the rest, and she never missed a step or forgot to keep her toes turned out.

POLLY [*A little more resigned, looks at the front of her dress and points to another patch*]: This one has roses and forget-me-nots on it. It's pretty—

GRANDMOTHER [*Breaking in*]: It ought to be, child, it came all the way from Paris and was a bit from Cousin Mariana Gay's best party sash.

POLLY: I never heard of her.

GRANDMOTHER [*Who is almost through fitting. She has been on her knees, hanging the skirt, but now she sits back on her heels as she tells* POLLY *about it*]: Why, she lived long ago, down South, and they say she was as pretty as her name. That's her guitar over there. She used to sit on her balcony, watching the boats go up and down the Mississippi River, and play and sing, "Listen to the Mocking Bird!" [*The* GRANDMOTHER *finishes hanging the dress and gets up, dusting her knees.*] There, now, that's fitted, and it's time you were in bed.

POLLY [*As her* GRANDMOTHER *helps her take off dress*]: Grandmother, I'd just as soon wear my brown dress and my red beads, if you shouldn't get this done in time.

GRANDMOTHER [*Folding up dress and bringing out* POLLY'S *nightgown*]: Who says I won't get it done by Friday?
[*Slips nightgown over* POLLY'S *head.*]

POLLY [*Hopefully*]: But that's tomorrow, and there are still a lot of stitches to sew.

GRANDMOTHER [*Smiling to herself as she helps* POLLY *into bed*]: I mean to get it done if my thimble finger drops right off! You just wait and see.

POLLY [*From the bed*]: Good night, Grandmother.

GRANDMOTHER [*Tucking her in and then going out with her candle*]: Good night, child, and pleasant dreams.
[*The stage should be dark for a minute or so after she has gone, and* POLLY *should lie perfectly still in the bed, as if asleep. Then we should hear someone offstage, calling as the Sea Captain's parrot did:* "Trim your sails and face the music!" *Twice, maybe three times. At each of these calls* POLLY *should*

start, move, sit up in bed and rub her eyes. The light in the room should be brighter now, but not too bright, for it must seem like a dream.]

POLLY [*Sleepily*]: That's funny.

[*Then into the light appears* GREAT-AUNT MEHITABEL *in her old-fashioned dress. If possible, she should have* GENERAL LA-FAYETTE *with her, and they should go through the steps of the minuet, while* POLLY *looks on with surprise.*]

POLLY [*Noticing her feet*]: You're Great-Aunt Mehitabel. You've got your toes turned out, just the way Grandmother said.

[GREAT-AUNT MEHITABEL *and her partner dance off, very dignified and precise.* POLLY *is just settling back under the bedclothes again when strains of music are heard offstage, and then* COUSIN MARIANA GAY *appears, in a full flowered dress, with the guitar with the yellow ribbons. She is playing on it and singing, "Listen to the Mocking Bird."* POLLY *bows to her from the bed politely.*]

POLLY [*As she enters and before she has begun singing*]: How do you do, Cousin Mariana Gay.

[COUSIN MARIANA *seats herself on the foot of the bed and begins to play the guitar and sing.*]

COUSIN MARIANA [*Singing*]:

> Listen to the mocking bird—
> Listen to the mocking bird—*

[*The little girl playing this part may sing one verse and the chorus if she wants, or just part of the chorus, but she should be playing and singing to* POLLY *as the curtain goes down.*]

Scene III

An old-fashioned schoolroom, with maps, blackboard and wooden benches for the scholars, stage center. Others for

---

* For the music for these words see *The Franklin Square Song Collection*, No. 6.

the visitors against the wall. POLLY *is all alone at the rise of the curtain, arrayed in her patchwork dress and looking very miserable. Sound of children's voices outside.* POLLY *looks off in the direction from which they come and half starts to get up.*

POLLY [*To herself*]: Oh, dear me, they're coming in now! They'll all begin to laugh at my dress. I wish I hadn't come. [*Looking toward another door.*] I could slip out through the entry. Nobody would see me, and I could stay out on the Common till it was time to go home.

[*She rises and takes a step or two, then stops, listening, for in a lull outside comes the voice of the Sea Captain's parrot off-stage, saying very distinctly:* "Trim your sails and face the music." *It is repeated three times, and* POLLY *returns to her place just as the scholars troop in.*]

ONE GIRL [*Pointing*]: Oh, my, just look at Polly!

ANOTHER [*Calling*]: See Polly's new dress all made of patches!

[*They gather round and whisper and point and laugh. Then* JIMMY WILLIS *pipes up teasingly.*]

JIMMY WILLIS [*Singing, alone at first*]:

> Polly Patchwork, now it's cool,
> Wears a crazy-quilt to school.
> Thinks she'll win the spelling match
> In her dress of patch—patch—patch!

[*The others join in, and* POLLY *hangs her head at first. Then, remembering the Sea Captain's parrot, she raises it and sits very straight. The* TEACHER *now enters, followed by the School Committee. There are three or four of them, the oldest one a man with whiskers and spectacles. Several parents have also come to look on. There can be as many or as few of these as desired. All wear old-fashioned clothes; the men have long coats, waistcoats, etc.; the women shawls, bonnets, capes and mitts.*]

TEACHER [*Standing behind her desk, rapping on it with ruler*]: The class will please come to order. Everybody eyes

front; hands folded. Don't fidget so, Rebecca Jones, and Willie Simpson, take your feet out of the aisle. That's better. Now you all know this is the last day of the fall term and a very important one for all of us, for the School Committee has come all the way from Cranberry Common to be here this afternoon and listen to the spelling match. Mr. Tippet will say a few words to you before we begin.
[*She sits down, and the oldest member of the School Committee rises, wipes his spectacles, clears his throat and begins.*]

MR. TIPPET [*Very pompously*]: Boys and Girls [*clearing throat*]—a-hem, a-hem—we have come all the way over here this afternoon to see how much you know about spelling. Spelling—a-hem, a-hem—is a very important subject for everyone to know. I once heard of a boy who wrote "h-o-l-e" in a letter when he meant "w-h-o-l-e," and it changed his entire life. So, boys and girls, you can't be too careful about spelling, and that is why—a-hem, a-hem—we have decided to present this medal to the best speller here— [*He takes medal from box in his pocket and holds it up on its ribbon.*]—this solid silver medal that any one of you may be proud to wear. [*The scholars clap and lean forward to see.*]

TEACHER [*Reprovingly*]: Back in your places, now. You can look at it afterwards. [*Hands book.*] I have asked Mr. Tippet to give out the words. [*Beckoning to them.*] Line up in your places now as I call your names.
[*As she calls each name, a pupil rises and takes his or her place.*]

Mary Jane Peters
Jimmy Willis
Rebecca Jones
Willie Simpson
Fanny Jenkins
Peter Davis
Lucy Smith
Jerry Bush

[*There can be as many more as the director thinks best, but* POLLY *must be called last.*]

POLLY MEHITABEL GAY

[*As she takes her place at the foot of the line, there are smothered snickers from her schoolmates, and they peer at her and make remarks to one another.*]

ONE VISITOR [*Low to her neighbor*]: What child is that in such an outlandish dress?

ANOTHER: Oh, that's little Polly Gay. Did you ever see such a figure as she cuts?

ANOTHER: I declare if it isn't a crazy quilt she's got on. Whoever heard of such a thing?

[POLLY *hears them and hangs her head. Tries to press her skirts down with her hands, but they will not flatten. As she does so, she smooths the yellow patch, the one that had belonged to* GREAT-AUNT MEHITABEL. *She touches this so that it is plain to the audience that she is remembering the minuet and what her* GRANDMOTHER *told her. Then, very carefully, she turns out her toes and holds up her head. This should all be done slowly so that people looking on will understand what is going on in* POLLY'S *mind.*]

TEACHER: Ready now, boys and girls. [*She nods to* MR. TIPPET *to begin.*]

[*He clears his throat and holds up the spelling book close to his spectacles, repeating each word very slowly and then peering over the book at the pupil who is to spell it. It is a very solemn occasion, and everybody listens breathlessly. The* TEACHER *nods when a word is spelled right and looks sorry when it is wrong.* MR. TIPPET *says "Correct," if it is right, and "Next" if it is wrong, in which case the scholar goes to his old seat. The spelling match can be as long as it seems best, beginning with such simple words as "sure, such, school, scissors"* [*for* POLLY *after her neighbor had missed it*], *"cheese, receive, believe, neighbor, weigh," etc., etc., getting more difficult, and more and more children drop out, till only six are left, with*

Polly still at the foot.]

MR. TIPPET [*Clearing his throat very loudly*]: Spell Mississippi.

MARY JANE PETERS [*Begins all right, then falters*]: Mis-is-i— [*She goes down crying.*]

TEACHER. You try, Jimmy.

JIMMY [*Very cocksure at beginning and then getting all mixed up*]: Mis-s-s-s-s-s-s [*He ends sounding like a hissing goose*].

MR. TIPPET [*Shaking his head*]: Next.

[*The others try, and each one forgets either an S an I or a P. At last* POLLY *is left all alone. The visitors and pupils all lean forward to listen. The schoolroom is very still.* POLLY *hesitates, it is plain she doesn't know how the letters ought to go. She looks down at her dress and sees the flowered patch, which she touches as she begins.*]

Mi— [*She stops, then says in a low voice, yet loud enough for the audience to hear.*] Oh, Cousin Mariana Gay, please help me to spell it right.

[*Strains of "Listen to the Mocking Bird" sound softly, and then a voice offstage saying distinctly: "Mi-double s—i double s—i—double p—i." Polly repeats it after her, slowly and distinctly. Adds "Oh, thank you, Cousin Mariana Gay." When she gets through, everyone claps and stamps his feet. The pupils all gather round her, and the* TEACHER *takes her hand and leads her up to* MR. TIPPET. *He brings out the medal and, with a deep bow, presents it to her while all the rest look on enviously.*]

MR. TIPPET [*Shaking hands*]: You are a very little girl to spell such a long word correctly.

TEACHER: Yes, Polly, I had never suspected you were such a good speller.

JIMMY WILLIS: Let me have a look at it, Polly, will you?

OTHER CHILDREN [*Crowding closer*]: And me—and me— I want to see it, *etc., etc.*

[*Just here* POLLY'S GRANDMOTHER *appears in the doorway, with a shawl and bonnet on, basket on her arm.*]

POLLY [*Seeing her*]: Why, Grandmother!

GRANDMOTHER: I thought I'd just stop by and see who won the spelling match. What's that you've got around your neck, child?

TEACHER: I am happy to tell you that Polly spelled a word all the others failed on.

GRANDMOTHER [*Pleased*]: My, my, just think of that now.

POLLY [*Going to her*]: It was Mississippi, Grandmother. [*Explaining earnestly.*] But I wouldn't have won it except for Cousin Mariana Gay and the Sea Captain's parrot and Great-Aunt Mehitabel—

MR. TIPPET [*Puzzled, with his hand to his ear*]: What's that the child is saying?

POLLY [*Going on*]: I didn't really know where all the s's and I's came, but I looked down at Cousin Mariana's patch hard [*she points to it on the front of her dress*], and I could see her as plain as plain on her balcony, playing the guitar and singing. So I asked her to help me, and she did. I said it right after her like this [*spelling as before*]: Mi—double s, i—double s, i double p—i.

GRANDMOTHER [*Listening and nodding her head wisely*]: Well, now, what did I tell you? It isn't everybody can have an experienced dress like yours to give them advice when they need it. [*To the others.*] We must go home now. Get your things, Polly, and run on ahead of me to get a basketful of cones to start the fire!

Curtain

Not on the Menu

BY MARY THURMAN PYLE

Characters

BARBARA ANDERSON, *14, capable and thoughtful*

JEAN ANDERSON, *12, whose imagination is sometimes almost too much for the family*

TOMMY ANDERSON, *11, whose friendly grin includes everybody*

"BUBBLES" ANDERSON, *8, a little girl who just bubbles over with good spirits and affection*

LESLIE NORRIS ⎫
BOB BROWN ⎭ *Friends of Tommy's*

AUNT HARRIET, *the Anderson children's great-aunt—a severe, plain-spoken, somewhat terrifying old lady*

Setting: The sun porch at the Andersons' house

NOT ON THE MENU
Reprinted from *Plays,* The Drama Magazine for Young People, 8 Arlington St., Boston 16, Mass. Copyright © 1942 by Plays, Inc.

NOT ON THE MENU

AT RISE: *The four Anderson children are discovered busily preparing for some unusual event. The furniture has been pushed back, and in the center of the room a heap of sticks has been laid, with three large sticks crossed at top, in imitation of a gypsy campfire. Other touches are about to suggest that the children have been converting the porch into a gypsy camp. At one end of a table,* BARBARA *is counting some kitchen knives and forks, and* JEAN *is pasting pieces of white paper onto the backs of old playing cards. There are five finished, and she is completing the sixth one.* BUBBLES *is fitting pieces of brown crepe paper over some empty jelly glasses, putting rubber bands around the tops of the glasses to hold the paper in place. There are already five glasses covered in this way, and she is completing the sixth.* TOMMY *is tying a piece of burlap over a low kitchen stool on which a sofa pillow is laid, the burlap to cover the whole, producing an irregular, lumpy object.*

BUBBLES: What are we *really* going to drink out of these jelly glasses, Barbara?

JEAN [*Quickly*]: They aren't jelly glasses! They're brown earthenware mugs. That's what gypsies would use—I think.

TOMMY [*Looking up from his job*]: I'll bet gypsies wouldn't have cocoa for supper, though.

JEAN: Now, Tommy! You promised you'd really play the

game. We've got to pretend the cocoa is a strange brew that only the gypsies know how to make—a secret recipe handed down to them.

TOMMY: O.K. But you've sure got some imagination, Jean. I'll bet you'd like to bring some real rocks in here to make the porch look more like a gypsy camp in the mountains.

JEAN [*Laughing*]: That's an idea! If there were time, I would. But that's a pretty good rock you're making.

TOMMY [*Surveying his handiwork*]: Some rock! And I have to sit on it, too.

JEAN: Well, if you want to be the king of this gypsy tribe, you've got to get in the spirit of it.

BUBBLES: I think Jean has a wonderful imag—imag— [*She is unable to remember the big word.*]

BARBARA: Imagination, darling.

BUBBLES: Imagination. That means she can make up swell stories, doesn't it?

BARBARA: Yes, Bubbles, it does—but Mother asked you *not* to say "swell." Remember?

BUBBLES: I won't, Barbara. But Tommy and the boys say "swell."

TOMMY: Sure we do. You practically have to. There's just no other word.—Say, how is this boulder for the gypsy king to sit on?

JEAN: That's *swell*—I mean, it's fine.

BARBARA: Just the thing—if it will hold you.

TOMMY [*Grinning as he sits on "rock" to test it*]: She works! I'm the king of the tribe—and that means you'll all do as I say.

JEAN [*Enthusiastically*]: Get your costume on. I'm just dying to see how you'll look.

BARBARA: I'll help you. [*She selects from the pile of accessories a red handkerchief, which she ties around her brother's head, a striped sash, which goes around his waist, a pair of curtain rings, with threads attached, which become earrings.*]

The chatter continues as she adds these colorful items to TOMMY's *ordinary costume of shirt and trousers.*]

TOMMY: Say, I don't know what Les and Bob will think of all this junk. [*Indicating the additions to his costume.*]

BARBARA: Oh, we've got some things for them to dress up in, too.

JEAN: And if those two kids don't behave at our party, they'll have to leave, that's all. Even if they are your special buddies.

TOMMY: Well, Mother said I could ask them, because tonight's our club night. And they're not kids. They're nearly as old as you are.

JEAN: All right—but if Leslie Norris and Bob Brown don't play like we want them to—

BARBARA: They will, Jean. I'm sure they will. Look! Doesn't Tommy look wonderful?

JEAN [*Her enthusiasm returning*]: Isn't this *fun?* And wasn't Mother a darling to let us have our supper like this?

BUBBLES: I wish Mother was here, too—and Daddy. [*Her chin begins to quiver.*]

BARBARA [*Quickly*]: Never mind, Bubbles. Mother won't be away for long—and we'll have Daddy home soon, I know.

TOMMY: These earrings won't stay on.

BARBARA: They will if you keep still.

JEAN: Imagine Tommy keeping still.

TOMMY: Sure I can!

BUBBLES [*Going to her brother and hugging him*]: Oh, Tommy, you look so sweet!

TOMMY: Sweet! [*His tone is one of great disgust at the very idea.*]

BARBARA [*Laughing*]: Well, take the earrings off till it's time to begin. There's more work to do before you can take your place on yon throne and boss us around.

JEAN: I'll say there is. Get the flashlights and see how the fire works.

TOMMY: I knew you girls would find more work for me to do.

BARBARA: But there're always a lot of things that only boys know how to do.

TOMMY [*Flattered*]: Oh, well— [*He goes out.*] I'll get the flashlights.

BUBBLES: I've finished the jelly glasses—[*hastily*]—I mean the—the—what kind of mugs did you say they were, Jean?

JEAN: Earthenware.

BARBARA: Come here, Bubbles, and let me fix you up. [BUBBLES *crosses to* BARBARA, *who adds beads and a head-dress to her little sister's outfit.*]

JEAN: And I've finished the menus. Don't they look *wonderful* on the backs of these old playing cards? You see [*to* BUBBLES] gypsies tell fortunes with cards, and that's how I got the idea of putting our menus on them.

TOMMY [*Returning with two flashlights*]: Here they are.
[*All bend over eagerly as he turns them on and places them among the twigs and brown paper which are on the floor in the center of the room, to give the effect of a lighted fire.*]

BARBARA: That looks wonderful! That was your idea, Tommy.

TOMMY [*With no false modesty*]: And a darned good one.

BARBARA: Tommy! Mother does so want us to grow up speaking nicely.

TOMMY: Well, if Daddy were here, he'd understand how a fellow has to say "darn" and "swell" sometimes.

BUBBLES: When will Daddy come home? Do you know, Barbara?

BARBARA: The doctor says he should stay at the sanatorium for several more months.

TOMMY: And he'll be all well then, won't he?

BARBARA: Yes—if he can just stay there a while longer.

JEAN: If only we could think of a way to keep him at the sanatorium. It seems like all of us together could raise the money—somehow.

TOMMY: What could a bunch of kids like us do to get the money? Gosh, I wish I were older. I could get a job.

JEAN: And so could I!

BARBARA [*Firmly*]: Now, listen, children! Mother doesn't want us to worry about things. She said so—very distinctly. The best we can do is keep happy and cheerful. Daddy would want that, too.

JEAN: There's Great-aunt Harriet!

TOMMY: Sure—and she could give Mother the money she needs, if she weren't a stingy old sourpuss.

BARBARA: Tommy, you mustn't say such things. Mother says if worse comes to worse, she'll ask Aunt Harriet for help, but you know Mother. She'll not ask unless there's no other way out.

BUBBLES: Maybe Aunt Harriet doesn't *know* Daddy is sick.

BARBARA: Of course she does—but perhaps she doesn't realize we need money so badly. Poor darling Mother has done everything she can to make some extra money.

JEAN [*With spirit*]: I'm not afraid of Aunt Harriet! I'll ask her for some money when she pays that promised call on us— If she really does come, which I doubt.

BUBBLES [*Hugging her sister*]: Jeannie! You're not afraid of anybody.

BARBARA: Of course we can't ask her for help. If it has to be done, Mother will do it. As a loan, of course. And Daddy must never know. He *must* believe we're getting along all right, or he hasn't as much chance to get well.

JEAN: And we *are* getting along all right! Aren't we having a marvelous time this very minute, with our gypsy dinner? [*This brings them all happily back to matters at hand.*]

BARBARA: Read the menu, Jean.

JEAN: I'm calling the stew "Hungarian goulash." There were Hungarian gypsies, weren't there?

BARBARA: There must have been.

TOMMY: But I'll bet their old goulash couldn't hold a candle to Mother's beef stew with vegetables.

BUBBLES: I wish Mother was here to eat it with us.

TOMMY: Trust Mother to drop everything to go sit with old Mrs. Andrews.

BUBBLES: Won't Mother have any dinner?

BARBARA: Of course she will, Bubbles. She'll probably have a delicious dinner, as well as the three dollars she'll make.

TOMMY: Old Mrs. Andrews is plenty rich. Mother will probably have chicken and ice cream and—

JEAN [*Briskly*]: But no fun! Now, besides the Hungarian goulash, I have down [*consulting her menu again*] "gypsy brew"—that's the cocoa. And for the rolls I wrote, "crusty bread baked fresh over the coals." We can pretend we really are toasting them, you see.

TOMMY [*Guffawing*]: Over the flashlights!

JEAN [*Glowering*]: Tommy! Are you going to play or not?

BARBARA: Of course he is. What else, Jean?

JEAN: Well, the apples and grapes we are supposed to have gathered as we traveled through the country.

TOMMY: Swiped 'em, you mean?

JEAN [*Dubious over the moral issue involved*]: Well—no. Maybe we worked in the orchards for them. It was hard to think up fancy names for just apples and grapes. I've heard of "apples of Hesperides."

BARBARA [*Superior*]: Oh, they were in Greek mythology.

TOMMY: There was a movie called *Grapes of Wrath*.

JEAN: But that didn't have anything to do with gypsies, silly. I thought "apples of happiness" sounded nice, and I've called the grapes "vintage grapes." [*Giggles.*] I don't know exactly what that means, but it makes them sound good.

BARBARA: Everything is ready to serve. Let's get dressed, Jean. The boys will be here soon.

JEAN: May I wear the orange-colored scarf? [*The two girls begin to add their embellishments. At this moment there is a war whoop from outside.* LESLIE *and* BOB *are approaching.*]

JEAN: Did you say the boys would be here?

TOMMY: Hot dog! It's Les and Bob. [*He goes to the porch door and unlocks it.* LESLIE *and* BOB *burst in. They are noisy, pleasant, average boys, about* TOMMY'S *age and his special cronies.*]

LESLIE [*Entering*]: Whoopee! Hey, everybody!

BOB: Hail, hail, the gang's all here!

LESLIE: What kind of eats are we going to have?

BOB: Is your mother out?

BARBARA [*Firmly*]: Yes, Mother's out. But that doesn't mean you boys can raise the roof.

LESLIE [*Taking in* TOMMY'S *costume*]: Hey, look at Tom!

BOB [*Bursting out laughing; quoting a popular song*]: "You ought to be in pitchers!"

BARBARA: "Pictures," Bob. "Pitchers" is simply dreadful.

BOB: Yeah, but the song says "pitchers."

TOMMY: You fellows have to dress up like this, too. Only I'm the king of the tribe, see. [*He struts about.*]

BOB: Oh, yeah! Then I'll be the prime minister.

LESLIE: And I'll be—who has charge of the food?—I'll be chief cook.

JEAN: Here, boys, put on your scarves and handkerchiefs.

BUBBLES: And put your earrings on.

LESLIE: Sure we will, Bubbles.

BOB [*With a bow*]: Anything Miss Bubbles Anderson asks, we will do!

LESLIE [*Bowing also*]: Bubbles, our future glamour girl!

BARBARA: We will eat as soon as we're all fixed. It's to be a gypsy supper, out here on the porch, you know. [*There is the sound of a long, firm ring at the doorbell. They all stand silent for a moment.*]

JEAN: Didn't Mother say we shouldn't answer the doorbell when she's out?

BARBARA: Yes, she did. [*The ring is repeated.*]

TOMMY: I'm not afraid. I'll go.

BARBARA: Wait, Tommy. Maybe they'll go away.

JEAN: Maybe we should telephone Mother.

BARBARA: Oh, no. She said not to phone her unless something really urgent came up.

BUBBLES: I'm—scared.

BARBARA: No, you're not, darling. Nothing could hurt us, with so many of us here.

LESLIE: Especially with all us fellows.

BOB: Let's scare 'em off, whoever it is. Come on—let's give the school yell. [*Without more ado, the three boys let out a war whoop of terrifying volume. The girls burst out laughing in spite of themselves. There is a sudden loud knock at the porch door. The laughers and the whoopers all stop in their tracks, frozen. The knock is repeated, followed by a sharp, feminine voice from outside.*]

AUNT HARRIET [*From outside*]: Why doesn't someone open this door? [*She shakes the door.*] Open this door! It's Harriet Anderson—it's your Great-aunt Harriet!

BARBARA [*In a whisper*]: Aunt Harriet! My goodness!

JEAN: What's she doing here? She wasn't supposed to come till next week.

TOMMY: Let's pretend we don't hear her.

BARBARA: Of all times! But we simply must open the door. After all, she is our aunt.

TOMMY [*Deprecatingly*]: Our *Great*-aunt!

AUNT HARRIET: Children! Don't you hear me?

BARBARA [*Going to the door and opening it*]: Hello! Do come in. You *are* our Aunt Harriet, aren't you?

AUNT HARRIET [*At door*]: Of course I am.

BARBARA: Please excuse us for not opening the door when you first knocked. We were frightened for a minute, because we're alone. Mother isn't here right now. [AUNT HARRIET, *tall, angular, rather forbidding, enters. She is about 60, gray-*

haired. She peers about in a curious but not unkind way.]

AUNT HARRIET: Oh! I'm sorry if I frightened you. [*Drily.*] I thought that you were merely making so much noise you didn't hear me.

BARBARA [*Apologetically*]: We were making a lot of noise, I guess.

AUNT HARRIET: And who are all these children? I didn't know the family was so large.

BARBARA: Oh, only four of us belong here. I'm Barbara.

AUNT HARRIET: The oldest. I remember you. Your father brought you to New York to see me once.

BARBARA: And this is Jean—she's twelve. And Tommy [*She draws* TOMMY *away from the other two boys.*] —this is Tommy—he's eleven. And this is the baby—she's eight.

AUNT HARRIET [*Looking them over appraisingly and stopping at* BUBBLES]: The youngest. Harriet! Named after me, your mother wrote me.

BUBBLES [*In innocent friendliness*]: I'm Bubbles.

BARBARA [*Hastily*]: You see, we thought "Harriet" sort of— sort of serious sounding for Bubbles. She is so—so *bubbling* over all the time. And she's such a happy little soul—

AUNT HARRIET: I see! You can't be happy if your name's Harriet, I presume. [*Fixes* LESLIE *and* BOB *with her glance. They stand in comical attitudes of embarrassment.*] Who are these?

TOMMY [*With his friendly grin*]: They are my special pals. We're the Three Musketeers—"One for all, and all for one." [*The boys go into position, with arms around each other's shoulders, in the famed Three Musketeers style.*]

AUNT HARRIET: You don't look like the Three Musketeers to me.

TOMMY: My goodness! I forgot these rigs.

JEAN: We're playing gypsy, Aunt Harriet. Mother said we could, while she was out.

AUNT HARRIET: Where is your mother?

BARBARA: She's—she's out on an errand. But I'll phone her right away to come home. [*She starts into the house.*]

AUNT HARRIET: Nothing of the sort! [BARBARA *comes back.*] It's all working out very nicely. I came on purpose at a time your mother wasn't expecting me. And with her out—that's even better. You can tell a great deal about a family if you study the children of that family when the parents aren't around. Well, aren't you going to ask me to sit down? And have dinner with you?

BARBARA: Of *course!* Where are our manners! [*The three girls help* AUNT HARRIET *off with her coat and hat. Gradually the atmosphere thaws, as, childlike, they begin to take their aunt into their jolly evening's plans.*]

JEAN: It's a funny dinner—but we think it's going to be fun. It's a gypsy dinner.

BARBARA [*Explaining, as the eldest*]: You see, Mother had to be out for a few hours, and she left our dinner all ready— it's a beef stew—

JEAN [*Clapping her hand over* BARBARA'S *mouth*]: No, it *isn't!* [*To* AUNT HARRIET.] We're playing it's gypsy food, and we've a menu, pasted on the backs of old playing cards.

BUBBLES: And I fixed the jelly—[*catching herself*] the earthenware mugs. There aren't but six, but you can have mine.

TOMMY: And I'm the king of the tribe.

LESLIE: I'm the prime minister. Do gypsies have prime ministers?

BOB: I'm head-man in the food department.

JEAN: And all of this is gypsy camp. We're going to eat out here on the porch. Mother said we could.

AUNT HARRIET: Where *is* your mother, may I ask?

BARBARA: She is staying with one of our neighbors who is an invalid.

AUNT HARRIET: Very commendable—if she doesn't neglect her family.

TOMMY: She gets three dollars for it—and we sure need the money.

BUBBLES: For Daddy.

BARBARA: Children!

AUNT HARRIET: Oh, I see.

BARBARA [*Quickly*]: Don't let's bother Aunt Harriet with things like that. We want you to have a good time, Aunt Harriet.

JEAN [*Inspired*]: You can dress up. We've plenty of beads and scarves.

TOMMY: And you can sit on this rock if you want to—[*grinning*]—only it isn't really a rock and might break with you.

AUNT HARRIET: In that case, I'll take the armchair.

JEAN: But not before you've dressed up like a gypsy. Here, let me fix you. [*She and* BARBARA *tie a bright handkerchief around* AUNT HARRIET's *head, before she can protest—if she meant to protest—and put some beads around her neck.*]

BUBBLES: Oh, you look so *nice*, Aunt Harriet. Let me put some bracelets on you. [*She stands against* AUNT HARRIET's *knee and slips a bracelet over her wrist.*]

BARBARA: Boys!—I mean, prime minister and chief cook—bring on the dinner! The king of the tribe will show you where it is, while we entertain our honored guest. [*She bows before* AUNT HARRIET, *and the rest follow her lead, all laughing merrily. The three boys march out in style, executing an "About, face! Forward, march!"*]

JEAN: Here's our menu, Aunt Harriet. It's just crazy names for what we are going to have. [AUNT HARRIET *takes the "menu" and studies it, a little smile beginning to play about the corners of her mouth.*]

BARBARA: I'm sorry you struck us on stew night. Mother says beef stew with vegetables is healthy and *filling*—for a bunch of children.

BUBBLES [*Innocently*]: And it's cheap.

BARBARA: Bubbles! *Ssh!* [*The boys return, bringing in an old-fashioned iron kettle, the handle of which they have put across a broomstick. They set it down over the make-believe fire.*]

LESLIE: Goulash! Lemme at it.

BOB: This stuff smells swell, no matter what you call it.

TOMMY [*Taking his place on his "throne"*]: Bring on the eats!

BUBBLES [*Very seriously*]: You mustn't say "swell" and "eats." [*They all laugh at her manner.*]

JEAN: Oh, this is such fun! Don't you *love* being a gypsy, Aunt Harriet?

TOMMY: I think you ought to be the gypsy queen, Aunt Harriet.

BARBARA: I *do* hope you don't mind pretending with us.

AUNT HARRIET: Not at all. I rather imagine I'll have a very enlightening—*and* entertaining time of it. And before the dinner is served, may I quote some words apropos to the occasion. They are words a real gypsy once said: "There's night and day, brother, both sweet things. There's the sun and stars, brother, all sweet things. There's the wind in the heath." [*There is a pause.*]

JEAN [*Sighs*]: That's *beautiful!*

AUNT HARRIET [*Softly*]: I hadn't thought of those words for years.

BUBBLES: I *like* you, Aunt Harriet.

TOMMY: Food! Food! That's a sweet thing, too!

LESLIE: I'll say! [*There is chatter and a clatter as the girls begin to serve the plates. The party is beginning to get into its stride as the curtain falls to indicate the passage of an hour or so.*]

AT RISE: MRS. ANDERSON *is seated at the table, and the four* ANDERSON CHILDREN *are grouped around her.* MRS. ANDERSON *is an attractive, energetic, but gentle and under-*

standing woman. She has just come in from MRS. ANDREWS'
*and has taken off her hat and coat, which lie on the table. She
is reading a note written on a piece of notebook paper. The
children show by their attitudes their affection for their mother
and their interest in what she is reading.*

MRS. ANDERSON: But what did your Aunt Harriet *say*,
Barbara?

BARBARA: She said she couldn't spend the night. I really
did urge her to, Mother.

JEAN: She said she'd go back to the hotel and drop by
again tomorrow.

TOMMY: And that she'd leave you this note. I gave her a
sheet of my notebook to write it on.

MRS. ANDERSON: I can't understand her coming before
the time she set for her visit. Did you explain why I was away,
Barbara?

BARBARA: Oh, yes, Mother. I think she understood.

JEAN: And she had a wonderful time at our party—didn't
she, Barbara? She dressed up and everything.

BARBARA: She certainly seemed to enjoy it.

BUBBLES: And she ate some of everything.

TOMMY: I'll say she was a good egg.

MRS. ANDERSON: Tommy!

TOMMY: I mean—a very nice—a very nice lady. We had
plenty of fun.

BUBBLES: I like Aunt Harriet. She let me put the jewelry on
her. And she liked the mugs I fixed out of the jelly glasses.

MRS. ANDERSON [*Reading the note*]: "Dear Charlotte."

BARBARA: What does she say?

JEAN: Read it out loud, Mother.

MRS. ANDERSON [*Begins to smile quietly as she continues
to read*]: "I attended a very wonderful dinner party this evening. I liked everything on the menu (that was really a very
tasty beef stew, besides being 'healthy and filling'), but I
particularly liked the things I found at that dinner which were

not on the menu. I shall give myself the pleasure of a more formal call tomorrow. Aunt Harriet." And here's a postscript. "Don't worry about the future, my dear Charlotte. 'There's night and day, brother, both sweet things.' H."

JEAN: She told *us* that, too. A gypsy said it.

BARBARA: But what does she mean by things not on the menu?

MRS. ANDERSON: I think I understand that. She meant [*looking at* BARBARA] tact and grace; [*looking at* JEAN] and wit and imagination. [*She rumples* TOMMY's *hair fondly as he grins at her*.] She meant friendliness and good-nature. [*She lifts* BUBBLES *to her knee*.] And affection. Yes, she certainly meant affection.

BUBBLES: She said I was named Harriet, but I said no, I was "Bubbles."

MRS. ANDERSON: You didn't! And you're supposed to be named after her. Oh, my goodness!

[*They are all laughing at their mother's tone of comic dismay, as the curtain falls*.]

PRODUCTION NOTES

Characters: 8.

Playing time: 20 minutes.

Costumes: The Anderson children wear regular school clothes, but have chosen the gayest things they have with the intention of appearing as gypsies by adding various bright colored scarves, sashes and jewelry. Tommy's friends are in everyday clothes.
Aunt Harriet is well dressed in dark clothes.
Mrs. Anderson wears an ordinary house dress.

Properties: Large sticks, knives and forks, pieces of white and brown paper, jelly glasses, rubber bands, burlap, kitchen stool, sofa pillow, bracelets, necklaces, earrings, two flashlights, kettle, broomstick, piece of note paper.

Setting: Sun porch furnished with wicker pieces, cushions covered in gay materials, a few potted plants here and there. The various accessories the children use are piled on a chair.

The Stolen Prince

BY DAN TOTHEROH

Characters

LONG FO, *the little son of the royal cook*

WING LEE, *his little sister, daughter of the royal cook*

THE ROYAL NURSE

HI TEE, *a poor but honest fisherman*

LI MO, *his wife*

JOY, *the stolen prince*

LEE MEE, *the duck*

TWO SOLDIERS OF THE ROYAL COURT

THE EXECUTIONER

THE CHORUS

THE PROPERTY MAN

THE ORCHESTRA

THE STOLEN PRINCE

The Stolen Prince is a play that appeals to many different age levels. It has been given by Fifth, Sixth and Seventh Graders with completely satisfying results on the part of the young actors and the responsive audiences.

Best results are attained with two casts, so that all members of the group who wish may have speaking parts. This makes it possible for the members of one cast to step into the parts of any actors in the other cast who might be absent for the final performance.

The members of the second cast become the orchestra for the first cast and vice versa.

The play is about a prince who was stolen at birth and rescued by a poor fisherman and his wife. They offend the emperor without meaning to and are sentenced to die. Recognition of the young prince saves the day for one and all and brings an heir to the kingdom.

Chinese plays give the actors plenty of freedom to use their imagination. The quaint, comic staging appeals to every audience, and the property man makes it not only humorous but easy as well.

Dan Totheroh wrote *The Stolen Prince* after seeing many amusing and colorful plays in the Chinese theater in his home city, San Francisco. He also wrote a sequel to this play entitled *The Lost Princess,* which is all about the fate of the twin sister of *The Stolen Prince.*

There is no stage setting, except for a back-drop of curtains and two black chairs, center. A lacquered box for the

PROPERTY MAN *stands in the left-hand corner. On the extreme right, separated from the players by a railing, is the* ORCHESTRA, *composed of three or more children dressed as Chinese men. They have no leader and they play without notes. Any instruments may be used, but there must be a gong. The music must be shrill and squeaky and, to our ears, discordant. Combs, covered with tissue paper, give a very good effect. A gong is struck by the* GONG-BEARER *and the* CHORUS *enters. He is dressed in a long mandarin coat and wears a headdress of feathers and beads. He walks very proudly to the center of the stage and bows. The gong is struck again and the* CHORUS *raises his hand.*

CHORUS: I am the Chorus and I am here to tell you all about the play that my honorable actors are about to act upon this stage. They are all waiting behind the curtain with their make-up on and they are very anxious to begin, so I shall be brief. [*The* ORCHESTRA *plays a few notes, stopped by the* CHORUS *raising his hand.*]

The name of our play is "The Stolen Prince." It is a sad story at first, but do not weep too hard, because it has a happy ending.

[*He claps his hands together. The* PROPERTY MAN, *a funny fellow in a black coat and trousers and a long queue enters and walks down stage, standing beside the* CHORUS.]

This is the Property Man. Bow! [*He strikes the* PROPERTY MAN *on top of the head with his fan and the* PROPERTY MAN *bows.*] He will change the scenery and will hand the properties to the honorable actors when they have need of them. And he will take especial charge of Lee Mee, the duck.

[*The* PROPERTY MAN *goes* "Quack! Quack!" *and the* CHORUS *strikes him again on the head with his fan.*]

CHORUS: Silence! It is not time for that! Are all your properties ready? [*The* PROPERTY MAN *nods his head.*] The first scene of our play takes place in the garden of the Emperor Lang Moo, in the Middle Flower Kingdom, a thousand and one years ago. [*The* GONG-BEARER *strikes the gong.*] It is spring-time and the blossoms are on the peach trees. It is a very important time in the household of the Emperor Lang Moo because a child is about to be born to him and he prays it will be a son. [*To the* PROPERTY MAN.] Where is the blossoming peach tree?

[*The* PROPERTY MAN, *who has been dreaming, starts and blinks; then shuffles up to the property box. He takes up a branch of imitation peach blossoms and, crossing to the two chairs, he stands behind them, holding the branch over them. Now and then he becomes tired of holding the branch in one hand and he carelessly shifts it to the other.*]

CHORUS: Long Fo and Wing Lee, a little sister and a little brother, children of the chief cook in the royal household, come under the peach tree to play together.

[*The* CHORUS *bows and steps to the left, where he stands throughout the play. There is music as* LONG FO *and* WING LEE *enter.*]

LONG FO: Will you help me fly my kite, Wing Lee?

[*At the word "kite" the* PROPERTY MAN *drops the peach branch and goes to the box, where he finds a paper kite on a short string. He gives it to* LONG FO, *then takes up the peach branch again.*]

WING LEE [*Sitting down on one of the chairs*]: There is not enough wind, Long Fo. Let us sit here beneath the branches of the peach tree and wait for news about the baby who is coming today.

LONG FO: I do hope it will be a boy.

WING LEE: Yes. If it is a girl, the Emperor will have her killed at once. Poor little thing!

LONG FO: Why are you so sorry for her? It is the law to kill girl babies because they are worth so little.

WING LEE: You say that because you are a boy, but I am very sorry for her.

LONG FO [*With contempt*]: You are a weak, weeping girl,

I am a big, strong man and I am going to fly my kite.

WING LEE: You cannot fly your kite because there isn't any wind.

LONG FO [*Sitting down*]: Then I shall wait patiently until the wind shakes the branches of the peach tree.

[*The* GONG-BEARER *strikes the gong three times, rapidly.*]

WING LEE [*Jumping up*]: What is it?

LONG FO: The new baby has come to the Emperor's palace.

WING LEE: Oh, I tremble with excitement!

LONG FO: I feel sure it is a boy.

WING LEE: And I feel sure it is a girl.

[*There is music. Enter the* ROYAL NURSE.]

LONG FO: Nurse! Nurse! Tell me! Is it a boy?

WING LEE: It is a girl, is it not, Nurse?

NURSE: It is both, my children!

WING LEE: Both?

LONG FO: How could that be?

NURSE: It is twins, my children. A boy and a girl.

[*The gong is struck. The* NURSE *and the* TWO CHILDREN *bow. They go out. The* PROPERTY MAN *takes the branch back to the corner and sits down on the box to rest.*]

CHORUS [*Bowing*]: The next scene of our illustrious play takes place in the same garden. Three days have passed. The nurse is walking in the royal garden with the royal twins. The day is warm and full of the perfume of peach blossoms.

[*The* PROPERTY MAN *returns with the peach branch and stands behind the chairs. The* NURSE *enters, carrying two dolls, one on each arm. One doll has a string of jade around its neck. That is the boy. The other doll is dressed in white and is the girl.*]

NURSE [*Sitting on one of the chairs and singing a little song to the twins*]: Go to sleep— Go to sleep— The wind is in the crooked tree.

[*The* PROPERTY MAN *waves the peach branch back and forth.*]

And it sings a song to you.

In the pool the goldfish three
are sleeping, too.
Go to sleep— Go to sleep— Go to sleep.
Go to sleep— Go to sleep— The moon is in the purple sky;
And it smiles a smile at you.
By the pool the dragon-fly
Is sleeping, too.
Go to sleep— Go to sleep— Go to sleep.

NURSE [*Speaking*]: Ah, my pretty babies, I love you both, but one of you must leave me. [*To the girl doll.*] Tomorrow you must die because you are a little girl.

[*The* PROPERTY MAN *hands her an embroidered silk handkerchief and she wipes her eyes, first one and then the other.*]

NURSE [*Holding up the doll with the string of jade around its neck*]: Ah, little one, you are the chosen of the gods because you were born a little boy. You will spend your happy childhood playing by the fish pond in the royal gardens. You will hear the Emperor's golden parrot sing and you will hear the sacred scarlet fish telling secrets to the sacred dragonfly. When you grow to be a man, you will become the Emperor of this great and mighty Middle Flower Kingdom. Bright is your shining star. [*Holding up the girl doll*]. Ah, dark is your star, little one. It is almost set. Tomorrow, at the hour of seven gongs, you die.

[*She wipes her eyes again. The gong is heard and there is music.*]

NURSE [*Looking off to the left*]: By the great green catfish, what do I see? A robber in the garden, stealing cabbages as plain as can be! I'll run and scare him away!

[*She places the two dolls on the chairs and runs off, waving her hands in the air. There is music.* LONG FO *and* WING LEE *enter.*]

WING LEE: Here they are. The nurse has left them alone. Now is our chance.

LONG FO: I do not approve of this, Wing Lee. If we are

found out, we will both have our heads cut off.

WING LEE: You promised to help me if I gave you my gold ball.

LONG FO: Oh, I'll help you all right. I never go back on my word, but I don't see what you want to save a girl for. They're so useless.

WING LEE: Quick! Don't talk any more. The nurse is coming back. Which is the girl?

LONG FO [*Lifting up the doll with the jade beads*]: This one, of course. She has jade beads around her neck.

WING LEE: Give her to me. Now let's run to the river.

[*They run off to the right. The* NURSE *returns and goes to the chairs. She starts back in surprise. She cannot believe her eyes—looks again—looks all about her—beats her breast.*]

NURSE: Oh! Oh! Oh! The prince has been stolen! Oh! Oh! Oh! I will have my head cut off for this! Oh! Oh! Oh! I must run away and hide myself in the mountains where they will never find me! Oh! Oh! Oh!

[*She runs off right, crying, taking the girl doll with her. The* ORCHESTRA *makes a terrible din.*]

CHORUS [*Bowing and raising his hand for silence*]: Our scene changes now. The action of our play moves from the garden of the Emperor Lang Moo to the green banks of the river Chang Hi. The Property Man will show you the river. [*The* PROPERTY MAN *puts the peach branch back into the box and takes out a piece of blue cloth. He unrolls it on the floor. He walks up and down on it, pulling up the legs of his trousers to show you the river is wet. Then he goes back to his box and sits down on it. He goes to sleep. There is music.* LONG FO *and* WING LEE *enter, running very fast and looking over their shoulders.* WING LEE *carries the doll with the jade necklace. She almost runs onto the blue cloth.*]

LONG FO: Be careful! Do not go too near the river, Wing Lee. You will fall in and be drowned!

WING LEE: Where is the tub?

LONG FO: [*Glancing at the* PROPERTY MAN, *who is still asleep*]: Yes, where is the tub?

[*The* PROPERTY MAN *snores.* LONG FO *looks helplessly at the* CHORUS.]

CHORUS [*Calling to the* PROPERTY MAN]: The tub! The tub! [*The* PROPERTY MAN *answers with another snore.*]

CHORUS [*To the audience*]: Excuse him, my good friends, for he is very stupid. We only keep him because we get him cheap.

[*He claps his hands loudly. The* PROPERTY MAN *jumps up as if he had been stuck with a pin. He looks about, bewildered.*]

CHORUS [*Severely*]: The tub!

[*The* PROPERTY MAN *takes a small wooden tub from the box and places it on the edge of the blue cloth. Then he goes back to his seat on the box.*]

WING LEE: Ah, there is the tub. We will put the little girl in the tub. The tub will float down the great river and some kind person will see it and give the poor little girl a home. [*She kisses the doll and puts it in the tub.*] Good-by, little girl. When I get back to the palace, I shall burn a stick of incense to the gods for your safe voyage down the great river. Ah, now it is in the current. There it goes!

[*The* PROPERTY MAN *shuffles over and pulls the tub slowly down to the other end of the blue cloth.* WING LEE *and* LONG FO *wave their handkerchiefs.*]

LONG FO: Now it has turned a bend in the river. It is out of sight. Let us go back to the palace, Wing Lee. I want to fly my kite.

WING LEE: There is not enough wind to fly your kite, Long Fo.

LONG FO: Oh, you always say that. Come on!

WING LEE [*Looking sadly down the river*]: There are many things can happen to her. A storm may rise and sink the tub. The terrible dragon-fish may see her and swallow her alive. Poor little girl, I fear for her. [*She wipes her eyes with her handkerchief.*]

LONG FO: Do not cry any more. You will get your eyes all red, and then they will begin asking questions at the palace. Come along! Come along!

[*He takes her hand and they go out. There is music.*]

CHORUS: And now we follow the wooden tub on its long journey down the great river of Chang Hi. It sails all that night and all the next day and stops, at last, before the houseboat of Hi Tee, a poor but honest fisherman.

[*He signals to the* PROPERTY MAN, *who fetches a stick with a white piece of cloth tacked to it to represent a sail. He sets this above the two chairs. Then he returns to the box and takes out the duck,* LEE MEE, *a stuffed duck with a big yellow bill, and places it in the center of the blue cloth. He stands back with arms folded as music and the gong are heard and* HI TEE *enters, followed by his wife,* LI MO. *They bow and sit side by side on the chairs.* HI TEE *rows the boat with imaginary oars.*]

HI TEE: I am that poor but honest fisherman named Hi Tee. This lady beside me is my wife, Li Mo. That [*pointing to the duck*] is our little duck, Lee Mee. He is a trained duck and the fish that he catches with his big bill he gives to us. We are very happy but we long for a child. Do we not, Li Mo?

LI MO: That is all that we need to make us completely happy.

HI TEE: All day long we sail and sail down the great river, Chang Hi, and little Lee Mee swims merrily behind us, catching us fishes as we go. See, the wind is shaking our sails. [*The* PROPERTY MAN *shakes the stick with the white cloth.*] Faster and faster now we go! The wind is so kind I shall not have to row any more today. I'll just sit still and watch the scenery go by.

[*He stops rowing with the imaginary oars. There is music.*]

HI TEE: But, merciful catfish, what do I see? A tub floating by, just as plain as can be!

LI MO: So it is! A tub—with a baby in it!

HI TEE: I'll jump into the water and save the child. A short way down the stream the dreadful rapids start. The tub will be upset and the baby will be drowned.

LI MO: Oh, save the child, Hi Tee!

[HI TEE *jumps from the chairs onto the blue cloth, and, making swimming motions with his arms, he picks up the tub and brings it back to the chairs.*]

LI MO: Give me the poor little baby. I shall take care of it and bring it up as my own child. [*She takes the doll and holds it in her arms.*]

HI TEE [*Looking at it*]: It is a baby of high degree. It wears a beautiful chain of jade about its neck.

LI MO: The gods have answered our prayers.

HI TEE: Lee Mee, our faithful little duck, we have another mouth for you to feed. Now, three times a day, you must catch three extra fish to feed our baby here.

[*The* PROPERTY MAN *gives an answering "Quack! Quack!" and shakes the sail.*]

LI MO: Here we go! Here we go! Floating down the water. We thank the gods for this little child—be it son or daughter!

[*The* PROPERTY MAN *quack-quacks again.* HI TEE *and* LI MO *rise, bow and go out, right. The* PROPERTY MAN *puts the wooden tub back in the box. The gong crashes. The* PROPERTY MAN *sits on his box and yawns. The* CHORUS *comes down and raises his hand.*]

CHORUS: The first act of our illustrious play is now over. You will excuse my actors while they are served a drink of tea to refresh themselves for the remainder of the performance? It is not easy work being actors, and they are tired.

[*He bows and goes out to the left. The curtain is not pulled. The* ORCHESTRA *spends its time tuning up, and then the actress who has played the* NURSE *enters with a tray of tea in little Chinese bowls and serves tea to actors and* ORCHESTRA. *They drink and return the bowls to the tray. The* NURSE *goes to*

56 _Entrances and Exits_

serve tea to the PROPERTY MAN _but finds him asleep, so, shrugging her shoulders, she leaves, drinking his bowl of tea herself. The gong is sounded. The_ CHORUS _re-enters and takes the center of the stage. He bows._]

CHORUS: Now that my actors have refreshed themselves, we will proceed with our play. Nine years have passed away. We are once more on the river Chang Hi, looking at the fishing boat of Hi Tee and his loving wife, Li Mo.

[HI TEE _and_ LI MO _enter and bow._ HI TEE _is wearing a gray cotton beard, the strings of which are tied around his ears._]

CHORUS: As you can see by Hi Tee's beard, he is not as young as he used to be. His wife, Li Mo, is not as young as she used to be, either, but she keeps her hair black by putting fish grease on it.

[HI TEE _and_ LI MO _take their places on the chairs._]

CHORUS: And now you will see the hero of our play, the little prince who was stolen. He does not know he is a prince, and you who are sharing the secret must not tell him or you will spoil him and he will become unhappy, longing for something he cannot have. His foster parents have named him Joy, which is a very good name for such a bright and laughing boy.

[_There is music._ JOY _runs in and bows. He wears the same chain of jade around his neck. It looks very strange with the rest of his coarse brown fishing costume. He turns to the chairs and waves to_ HI TEE _and_ LI MO. _They beckon him to come to them. He runs over to the chairs and sits between them._]

HI TEE: Where have you been all day, my little Joy?

JOY: I have been digging mud turtles with my friend, Kee Hee, but we did not find any. Then we looked for fish with our nets but we could not find any fish either. I am hungry now, dear Mother.

LI MO [_Shaking her head sadly_]: Alas, my poor boy, I am hungry, too, and so is your poor father, but there are no fish in the great river.

JOY: Why are there no fish in the great river?

HI TEE: Because, my Son, the gods are angry. They have tied strings to all the fishes' tails and are holding them prisoners in the tall mountains where the river begins.

LI MO: If they do not untie the strings and let the fish float down to us, very soon we will all die.

JOY: I will climb up the tall mountains to the place where the river begins and untie the fishes' tails. I am not afraid, Mother.

LI MO: The gods would kill you, my little Son, and then what would I do without you?

JOY: Cannot Lee Mee, our faithful little duck, find any fish, either?

LI MO: Can you find us any fish, Lee Mee?

[*They wait for a "Quack, Quack" from the* PROPERTY MAN, *but he is still asleep. The* CHORUS *turns and sees him sleeping. He crosses to him with great dignity and taps him on the head with his fan. The* PROPERTY MAN *leaps up, blinking.*]

CHORUS: You will be discharged after the play is over. You have not given us a "Quack"!

PROPERTY MAN [*Staring stupidly*]: Quack! Quack!

JOY: What does our little duck say?

PROPERTY MAN: Quack! Quack! Quack! Quack!

LI MO: He says he will search every river and every pond and every lake the whole world over until he finds a fish for us to eat.

JOY: I will go with him.

HI TEE: No! You must stay with us. Go, my good Lee Mee, and bring a fishie back to poor Hi Tee.

[*The* PROPERTY MAN *shuffles forward and picks up the duck and tucks it under his arm. He shuffles off with it, giving a solemn "Quack! Quack!"*)

LI MO: If there is a fish left in the river, the lake, or the pond, Lee Mee will find it for us. He is the most faithful duck in the whole Middle Flower Kingdom.

JOY: I love Lee Mee!

[*There is music.*]

CHORUS: An hour passes by and Lee Mee returns.

[*The* PROPERTY MAN *enters with the duck. He has put into the beak of* LEE MEE *a fish carved out of wood and painted a bright scarlet. He sets* LEE MEE *down close to the chairs; then returns to his box.*]

HI TEE: Look! Look! Lee Mee has found a fish for us!

LI MO: Oh, good Lee Mee!

JOY: I have never seen such a beautiful fish before. It is as red as blood.

HI TEE: It is very beautiful. Where did you get it, Lee Mee?

PROPERTY MAN: Quack! Quack!

LI MO: He says he will not tell.

JOY: Let us eat it at once. I am very hungry.

[HI TEE *reaches down and takes up the fish.*]

HI TEE: You may have the tail, Li Mo. I will have the head, and our son, the little Joy, may have the middle because it is the sweetest and the fattest. Give me my knife.

[*The* PROPERTY MAN *takes a long wooden knife with a curved blade from the box and gives it to* HI TEE. HI TEE *puts the fish on the edge of the chair and raises the knife over his head. The gong and loud music are heard.* TWO SOLDIERS *enter carrying tall bamboo poles. They point at the scarlet fish and rush at* HI TEE.]

FIRST SOLDIER: You are my prisoner!

HI TEE: What have I done?

PROPERTY MAN [*Mournfully*]: Quack!

FIRST SOLDIER: Come along! [*He picks up the fish. To the* SECOND SOLDIER.] Bring the rest of them.

[*He starts off with* HI TEE. *The* SECOND SOLDIER *follows with* LI MO *and* JOY. *As they are about to go out,* JOY *brushes aside the bamboo pole of the* SECOND SOLDIER *and rushes back to* LEE MEE, *the duck. He tucks it under his arm.*]

JOY: I would never leave you, Lee Mee! Never in the world.

PROPERTY MAN: Quack! Quack!

[JOY *rushes back to the* SECOND SOLDIER *and they all depart. The gong and music are heard.*]

CHORUS: And now we are back once more in the garden of the Emperor Lang Moo. It is the next morning. [*The* PROPERTY MAN *rolls up the blue cloth and takes the sail down from the chairs.*] It is autumn time when the leaves are falling. [*The* PROPERTY MAN *takes a handful of imitation autumn leaves from the box and walks solemnly across the stage, scattering them to left and right as he goes.*] It is the sad time of the year and all of the Emperor's court is sad because the Emperor is very ill. Everybody knows that the great Lang Moo will soon die and will pass above to the celestial kingdom. This is indeed sad in itself, but when an emperor dies without a son to take his throne, then it is tragedy.

[*The gong is struck and the* ROYAL NURSE *enters. She is walking with a cane, for she is now very old and bent.*]

NURSE [*Looking about her*]: Ah, me—ah, my—many years have passed since I was banished from this royal garden. I am a very wretched old woman. It is all my fault because the mighty Emperor is dying without a son. Ah, me—ah, my—[*She sits on one of the chairs and the* PROPERTY MAN *gives her a large silk handkerchief to weep into. She weeps, first wiping one eye and then the other.*] I do not know what brought me back today, but something whispered in my ear and said that I should come. I left my mountain hiding place and walked for three long nights and three long days. I am now so very old that no one will ever recognize me, so I am safe.

[LONG FO *and* WING LEE *enter. They are now grown up and wear older headdresses.*]

WING LEE: It is here the execution will take place.

LONG FO: Yes, and the Executioner should be here now. He

is always on time.

NURSE: Pardon me, my children, but may I ask who is going to be executed?

WING LEE: Oh, don't you know?

NURSE: No, I am a stranger here.

WING LEE: Four heads are coming off this morning. The head of a fisherman, the head of his wife, the head of his son and the head of a duck, Lee Mee.

NURSE: What have the poor souls done?

WING LEE: They have—

LONG FO: Let me tell her, Wing Lee. You are only a woman and you will get the story mixed up. [*To the* NURSE.] The little duck, Lee Mee, stole the Emperor's sacred scarlet fish from the royal fish pond and brought it to the fisherman and his family for them to eat.

NURSE: But if the duck stole the fish, why should they execute the fisherman and his family, too?

LONG FO: Because the duck belonged to the fisherman and the fisherman should have taught him better manners.

WING LEE: Oh, here comes the Executioner!

[*The* EXECUTIONER *enters, walking very proudly. The* PROPERTY MAN *hands him a wooden axe. The* EXECUTIONER *stands to one side as the gong sounds.* HI TEE *walks in very slowly with his head bent.* LI MO *enters next; then* JOY, *carrying the duck,* LEE MEE. *They are followed by the* TWO SOLDIERS. HI TEE, LI MO *and* JOY *form a straight line. The* TWO SOLDIERS *stand in front of them. The* PROPERTY MAN *gives the* FIRST SOLDIER *a scroll.*]

FIRST SOLDIER [*Reading from the scroll before him*]: Today, Hi Tee, fisherman on the river Chang Hi, his wife, Li Mo, their son, Joy, and the most evil, bad-mannered duck, Lee Mee—[*The* PROPERTY MAN *quacks sadly.*]—will die under the axe of the executioner.

[*The* EXECUTIONER *swings his axe.*]

The first to die will be the little boy named Joy, so that his parents may have the extreme pleasure of seeing the axe fall on his neck.

[*He motions to the* EXECUTIONER, *who steps forward.* JOY *kisses his father and his mother good-bye and then kisses* LEE MEE, *the duck, handing it to* HI TEE. *Then he steps bravely forward. He sinks to his knees and bows his head. The chain of jade is plainly seen around his neck. The* EXECUTIONER *raises his axe to strike.*]

WING LEE [*To* LONG FO]: I'm sure I've seen that chain of jade somewhere before.

FIRST SOLDIER: Wait, Executioner! I will remove this chain of jade. It is too beautiful to be cut by the Executioner's sword. I will keep it for my wife. [*He takes the chain from* JOY's *neck.*]

NURSE [*Jumping up*]: Oh, stay a moment! Where did he get that chain of jade?

FIRST SOLDIER: Who are you, old woman?

NURSE: You do not recognize me, for I am so very old, but I am Sing Lo, the royal nurse who long ago was banished from the court because the little prince was stolen while in my care. Do you remember?

WING LEE [*Suddenly beginning to weep*]: Oh! Oh! Oh!

FIRST SOLDIER: What is the matter with you?

LONG FO: She is not feeling well, sir.

NURSE [*To* JOY]: Where did you get that chain of jade?

JOY: It has always been around my neck, as long as I can remember.

NURSE [*To* HI TEE]: Is this your son?

HI TEE: Y—yes.

NURSE: Your true son?

LI MO [*Breaking down*]: He is not our true son, I must confess. We do not know who he is. We found him in a wooden tub, floating down the river, when he was only a tiny baby.

WING LEE: Oh! Oh! Oh!

NURSE: He is the stolen prince!

FIRST SOLDIER: What?

WING LEE: It's true.

FIRST SOLDIER: What do you know about it, Wing Lee?

WING LEE: I was the one who stole him.

NURSE: You?

WING LEE: Yes, when I was a little child, the nurse had left the twins beneath the peach tree. They were going to kill the little girl, so I thought I would steal her away. By mistake, I stole the little prince. I sent him down the river in a wooden tub, with that chain of jade around his neck.

JOY [*Jumping up*]: What are you all talking about? Aren't you ever going to cut off my head? I'm tired of waiting.

NURSE [*Taking him in her arms*]: We are not going to cut off your head. Instead, we are going to put a crown on it. You are the royal son of the mighty Emperor Lang Moo, who now is dying in his royal bed. The throne of the Middle Flower Kingdom will soon be yours.

FIRST SOLDIER: I will run and tell the Emperor.

SECOND SOLDIER: And so will I!

[*They run out.*]

LONG FO [*To* WING LEE]: What did you say anything for? Now we will be beheaded.

NURSE: Oh, no, you won't. The Emperor will be so glad to get his son back that he will smile to the end of his days.

JOY: Is it really true I am the Prince? Mother, is it really true?

LI MO: Yes, my little Joy. [*She weeps.*]

JOY: Why do you weep, Mother?

LI MO: Because you will become the Emperor and I shall never see you again.

JOY: Oh, yes, you will, Mother. You will always be next to my heart. You and Father and Lee Mee will always be my dearest dears.

PROPERTY MAN: Quack! Quack!

[*The* FIRST *and* SECOND SOLDIERS *return.*]

FIRST SOLDIER: Little Prince, the Emperor awaits you in the royal bedchamber. Will His Royal Highness come?

JOY: May I bring my family along, too?

FIRST SOLDIER: Of course, Your Highness.

JOY [*Taking* LI MO's *hand*]: Come along, Mother. You and I will go in together. Hi Tee, you and Lee Mee follow close behind.

[*Music and gong are heard as in procession,* JOY *and* LI MO, *followed by* HI TEE, *carrying* LEE MEE, *go out. The* TWO SOLDIERS *close in at the last.*]

LONG FO [*To the* EXECUTIONER]: Why do you pull such a long face, Executioner? Are you angry because you couldn't use your axe?

EXECUTIONER [*Growling*]: *Burrrr!* [*He shoulders his axe and stalks off.*]

NURSE: Let us tiptoe down to the royal hall and peek through the royal keyhole into the royal bedchamber. I would like to see the Emperor greet his little son.

[*There is music. With fingers on lips and stepping very high on tiptoes, they start off in line, led by the* NURSE. *The* PROPERTY MAN *starts to follow.*]

CHORUS: Stop!

[*The* PROPERTY MAN *stops. The others go out.*]

CHORUS: You cannot peek through the royal keyhole because you are only the Property Man.

PROPERTY MAN [*Hanging his head*]: Quack! Quack!

CHORUS [*Stepping forward and bowing*]: My good and patient friends, our play is over. For your kind attention, I bow and bow and bow.

[*He bows three times. The* PROPERTY MAN *bows three times.* CHORUS *turns and sees him.*]

CHORUS [*Snapping his fan open with great dignity*]: You are discharged!

[*He sweeps off to the left. The* PROPERTY MAN *shrugs his shoulders and goes out to the right.*]

The curtain is pulled back, showing tableau of all the characters grouped around JOY, who is seated on one of the black chairs with a crown on his head. In his arms he holds Lee Mee, the duck. Li Mo stands next to him and, on the other side, Hi Tee.

PRODUCTION NOTES

No special production notes are given for this play besides those incorporated in the directions throughout the script. Some of the educational values inherent in producing a Chinese play come from the research done by the children as they delve into the fields of Chinese stagecraft, art, costuming, scenery properties and music. Reversible screens with painted panels appropriate to the setting are always the easy solution as far as scenery is concerned.

Under the Skull and Bones

A PIRATICAL PLAY FOR BOYS AND GIRLS

BY RONALD GOW

Characters

BERT
TOM   } *scouts*

CAPTAIN CUTLASS

SLIT-GIZZARD BILL

SNOOKS

RAMROD

BLOODWINKLE

SLIMY

BLUE-NOSED PETE AND OTHER PIRATES

A POLICEMAN

UNDER THE SKULL AND BONES

Under the Skull and Bones was written for boys. However, it has been staged and acted by girls and also by a mixed cast.

The three tunes to which the songs are set can be found in *Songs of the British Isles,* published by Curiven and Sons Ltd.

The pirates have a hard time deciding whether to make Tom and Bert walk the plank or to give them a nice, easy death by hanging.

Scene I

SCENE—*A quay-side after dark. A barrel in the center. The light is very dim, except where the gleam from some lamp falls on the center of the stage. Enter Two Scouts. They advance to the center of the stage with silence and cunning. The silence is broken by* TOM's *pole, which, by some strange mischance, has fallen to the ground.*

BERT: Silly ass!

TOM: It fell.

BERT: *Ssh!* [*He peers round the barrel.*]

TOM: Can you see anything?

BERT: I thought—look there, out at sea.

TOM: There's nothing.

BERT: I thought I saw a light.

TOM: I can't see anything. But my eyes are all funny with staring.

BERT: There doesn't seem to be anybody about. But this is the place.

TOM: Yes, this is the place, and I'm not going till we get to the bottom of this mystery.

BERT: What time is it?

TOM: About nine. It was just this time when we saw the light.

BERT: And three nights running! It's all so jolly mysterious.

TOM: It seemed to me to be short flashes—one after the other. Just like somebody signaling out to sea.

BERT: Of course I've heaps of theories, but theories should be based on facts, and we haven't really got many of those, have we?

TOM: Oh, I don't know. A flashing light is a pretty big fact. Lights don't flash unless somebody flashes them.

BERT: I say, Tom, that's jolly true, and it's not bad for you. Now my best theory is *spies*.

TOM: Spies? There's no war.

BERT: Well, that's just the time for spies. You know, they may be getting one up. What's that? [*They peer again.*] I'll swear that was a flash.

TOM: I didn't see it, Bert.

BERT: It's all a question of keeping your weather eye skinned. I always do it. It seemed to come from there— about the middle of the bay.

TOM: Right, I'll watch. Tell me some more theories.

BERT: Well, my next best theory is Pirates.

TOM: Pirates? But there aren't any.

BERT: Oh, aren't there? Old Bill Stevens says he was a pirate—anyway he chews tobacco. Besides, what I say is this —if there aren't pirates nowadays, why aren't there? It's a jolly exciting way of making a living, and if I hadn't been a Scout and on the side of the law and all that sort of thing— well, I'd have thought about it. Can you see anything?

TOM: No.

BERT: Well, what are you blinking for? Are you sleepy?

TOM: I'm not sleepy. It's just my eyes.

BERT: What time have you got to be home?

TOM: There'll be a row if I'm not home by half past.

BERT: Same here. It's absolutely rotten. Never gives a chap a chance. And they've got simply no imagination at home. They'd never believe how serious this is.

TOM: It's beastly. [*A pause.*] I say, Bert. [*They settle down with their backs to the barrel.*]

BERT: Yes?

TOM: I like the pirate theory best.

BERT: So do I—really. Spies are more likely—but pirates are best.

TOM [*Sleepily*]: Pirates are fine . . .

BERT [*Yawning*]: Pirates don't fit the facts, though. You've always got to consider the facts. No, I don't really believe . . . only . . . I wish there were . . . pirates.

[TOM *mumbles—and they are both asleep. Then a strange thing happens. A pirate rises out of the barrel. He produces a lantern and flashes it. Then he blows a shrill blast on a whistle. Enter the Pirate* CREW.]

CAPTAIN: Tumble up there, ye vile cutthroats! Heave to and harken to me! I have a new song to sing ye! [*The* CREW *groan.*] Thunder and lightning! [*The* CREW *cheer.*] That's better. [*He sings.*] *

CAPTAIN [*Singing*]:

> Now I'm a pirate bold,
> Like those in days of old,
> Who sailed the Spanish Main
> I've a scoundrel crew
> Of rascals fierce and true,
> Whose villainy is very plain.
> And it's yo-heave-ho!
> There's room for you below,

* Tune: "Lady Frances Nevill's Delight."

In the locker of old Davy Jones.
For we fly the Skull and Bones,
And our hearts are stones—
You'll be company for Davy Jones!
Oh, at my yard-arm-end,
My prisoners I bend,
And watch them dance on air.
Or a merry prank
Is to make them walk the plank,
While we watch to see they do it fair.
And it's yo-heave-ho!
There's room for you below,
In the locker of old Davy Jones.

ALL:

For we fly the Skull and Bones,
And our hearts are stones—
You'll be company for Davy Jones!

[*They march around the sleeping Scouts and then take up positions at the back, their malignant faces gleaming in the dim light.*]

CAPTAIN: Abaft and belay there! Ye lily-livered swabs! Put a reef in your gaskets! Where's Slit-Gizzard Bill? [*A Pirate comes forward and salutes.*]

BILL: Aye, aye, Cap'n!

CAPTAIN: Dog!

BILL: Aye, aye, Cap'n!

CAPTAIN [*Turning livid with anger*]: None o' your lip, now, ye deck-swabbing lubber! Hast landed the goods?

BILL: Aye, aye, Cap'n. The goods is landed. If ye please, Cap'n, the men want to ask a respectful question.

CAPTAIN: Question! Out with it! [*He draws a pistol.*] And maybe, if the question isn't to my liking, I'll ask a few myself —with this! [*He pats the pistol. The men shrink back.*] Now then, ye dried codfishes, what about that question? Well, ain't none o' ye got the guts to ask it? Come here, Snooks, let's have a look at ye. [SNOOKS *slinks forward.*] Smell that! Now what's the question? The respectful question, eh?

SNOOKS [*Shivering*]: *Brrrrr!* I've f-f-f-f-forgotten it!

CAPTAIN: Oh, ye've forgotten it, have ye, ye mutinous swab! Then, if ye don't remember it quick, ye'd better say your prayers! [*The* CREW *growl.*] Mutiny, eh? Thunder and lightning! Silence atween decks there, or I'll let the daylight into a few of ye! Come on now!

SNOOKS [*Still stammering*]: We would l-l-like to know, r-r-r-respectful-like, if it's equal s-s-shares in this b-b-business?

CREW: Aye, equal shares! Man and man alike!

CAPTAIN [*Furious*]: Brimstone and treacle! Ye vile bottle-washers! So that's the little game, is it! I'm Captain here, and it's me divides the shares. Down on your knees, ye black villains, and beg for mercy! Down on your knees, I tell ye, or by Davy Jones, I'll see the color o' your insides!

[*One by one, the* PIRATES *go down on their knees. Satisfied, he struts up and down before them, singing to the previous air.*]

> Now all indiscipline,
> I count a horrid sin,
> As all my crew well I know.
> I've a pistol here
> Which answers loud and clear,
> A mutiny with me won't go.

[CREW *here sway their bodies in time.*]

> And it's yo-heave-ho!
> There's room for 'em below,
> In the locker of old Davy Jones.

ALL [*Marching round*]:

> For we fly the Skull and Bones,
> And he likes our groans—
> We'll be company for Davy Jones.

[*The* CREW, *with the exception of* SLIT-GIZZARD BILL, *march out, singing the chorus.*]

CAPTAIN: That's my way with a mutineering crew! I'll larn

'em to ask respectful questions! Now, Bill, what's to be done with this pair o' landlubbers? [*He indicates the sleeping* SCOUTS.]

BILL: Make 'em walk the plank, Cap'n.

CAPTAIN: Walk the plank, eh? That's getting rather over-done. We want some new notions.

BILL [*Rolling his eyes*]: Make mincemeat of 'em!

CAPTAIN [*Smacking his lips*]: Mincemeat, eh? Aye, there's something in that. I've a serious charge against this one. Says he doesn't really believe in pirates. I overheard 'em from the barrel. That comes o' modern education, Bill. Howsomever, they both confessed a liking for pirates, so I've a mind to be lenient with 'em. What d'ye say to a gentleman's death by hanging at the yard-arm?

BILL: Yah! The men want blood!

CAPTAIN: Avast there! I'm Captain here, and I'll have my way with prisoners! Rouse 'em up! [BILL *proceeds to waken the* SCOUTS *with his toe.*]

BERT [*Rubbing his eyes and yawning*]: O-oh! Wake up, Tom. [*He sees the* PIRATES.] Golly!

TOM: Hello!

BERT: I say, Tom, look there!

TOM: Ooo! Pirates!

BERT: Pirates don't fit the facts.

TOM: I think it's my eyes again. [*He rubs them.*]

CAPTAIN: Oh, so we don't fit the facts, don't we?

BILL: Shoot the dog, Cap'n!

CAPTAIN: Silence! This ugly fish is my mate, Slit-Gizzard Bill by name, who's slit more gizzards than any man sailing the seven seas, barring myself. Captain Cutlass is my name, and I've a crew of murderous blaggards under me. Are we to understand from your remarks that you don't believe in pirates?

BERT: Well, not really.

BILL [*Advancing with his knife*]: Blood! Blood! [BERT

jumps to his feet and raises his pole. BILL *takes cover behind the* CAPTAIN.]

CAPTAIN: Thunder and lightning! I may be a pirate, but I'll have justice for my prisoners. Put that knife up, ye jellyfish!

BERT: What do you mean by saying we are your prisoners?

TOM: It's quite the other way. We arrest you on a charge of—well, whatever you've been doing.

CAPTAIN [*Laughing*]: Ho! Ho! Ho! Hark at 'em, Bill! [*The* PIRATES *laugh uncontrollably.* BERT *crosses to the* CAPTAIN *and digs him in the ribs with his pole.*]

BERT: Stop that beastly row, can't you?

CAPTAIN [*Furious*]: Shiver me timbers, but ye'll suffer for that! I'll show ye what I mean by prisoners!
[*He blows a whistle. The* CREW *appear and take up position with their weapons ready.*]

CAPTAIN: Well, what d'ye think o' that?

TOM: I think it's rather like a pantomime. [*The* CREW *growl.*]

CAPTAIN: Seize those men and take 'em on board!

BERT: Stop! I warn you that we are Scouts of the 3rd Muggleton Troop, and if a hair of our heads is harmed, you will pay a terrible penalty!

CAPTAIN: Stow that, ye lily-livered landlubber!

CREW: Blood! Blood! Slit his windpipe! Boil 'em in oil!
[*And other pleasantries. The* SCOUTS *are seized and bound.*]

CAPTAIN: March 'em on board and put 'em in irons! I'll show who's Captain on my vessel! Shake out the mainsail, lads, and yo-ho for the Spanish Main!
[*Singing.*]

>   And it's yo-heave-ho!
>   There's room for 'em below,
>   In the locker of old Davy Jones.

ALL [*Marching*]:

>   For we fly the Skull and Bones,

And our hearts are stones—
They'll be company for Davy Jones!
[*They march out with the prisoners.*]
    Curtain

    Scene II

    SCENE—*On board the pirate ship. A sail at the
back. Some ropes and rigging hanging about. There are a
cannon and some kegs marked "Rum" and "Powder."* SNOOKS
*sits on the cannon fiddling, while another of the pirates dances
a hornpipe in the center. The other pirates are grouped
around, shouting encouragement and beating time.* CAPTAIN
CUTLASS *calls for silence. He sits beside a barrel marked
"Powder."*

    CAPTAIN: Avast and belay there! Batten your hatches and
harken to me! I'm in a thoughtful mood. Give me a noggin of
rum! Rum, ye scabs, rum! Serve out rum to every swab
aboard! We've serious business this morning. First of all,
there's gold, red gold to be shared out.

    CREW: Hooray! [*They dance and throw their caps in the
air.*]

    CAPTAIN: Silence, ye mutinous scum! I'll make every man
jack walk the plank if there's any more o' that! Next business
will be the pleasant and gratifying performance of disposing
of the prisoners.

    CREW [*Smacking their lips*]: Blood! Blood!

    CAPTAIN: Aye, ye'll have blood all right. But not till I
give the word. I'm Captain here. We'll have the usual court-
martial. First of all, I call upon Blue-Nosed Pete to favor us
with a song in celebration of this momentous occasion.

    CREW: A song! A song! Blue-Nosed Pete! [BLUE-NOSED
PETE *comes forward and clears his throat.**]

    PETE [*Singing*]:

    * Tune: "The Buff Coat."

> Yo-heave-ho!
> There's captives down below.
> Hang 'em and draw 'em,
> And hack 'em and saw 'em,
> And make 'em walk the plank-o;
> Thumbscrew and nine-tails,
> A rope's end if that fails,
> And won't they like the plank-o.

ALL: Bravo! [*They repeat it in chorus.*]

CAPTAIN: A very excellent and tasteful song! Give us another verse in praise of rum.

PETE:

> Deep, brown rum!
> What'd we do without our rum-o!
> Drives away sorrow,
> And cares of the morrow,
> What need have we to look glum-o?
> Makes a man jolly,
> And ready for folly,
> With a rumpty-ti-tum-ti-tum-o!

[*They sing it in chorus and drink large quantities of rum.*]

CAPTAIN: Belay there! We now come to the matter of gold.

CREW: Gold! Red gold! Share and share alike!

CAPTAIN: Silence atween decks! Slit-Gizzard Bill, bring forth the Treasure Chest.

[BILL *drags forward a chest. The* CREW *make an ugly rush, but the* CAPTAIN'S *pistol copes with the situation.*] Back, hounds! Listen to me, ye mutinous dogs. I've a word to say on the matter of thrift. How many of ye has a savings account? [*Silence.*] Not a blessed one! Then how many of ye has a money-box? [*Another shamed silence.*] Boys, not one of ye with a penny laid by for a rainy day! This is very shocking. My heart is considerably saddened. However, I have a plan. We'll have equal shares of this gold—but only on condition that every man of ye opens a savings account with me. What say ye to that?

CREW: We want our gold!

CAPTAIN: Of course, and you'll get it. But it will be safer with me in this box. You'll be glad of it some rainy day.

CREW [*All talking angrily at the same time*]: It's no good! We want our gold! Share and share alike! [*Etc.*]

CAPTAIN: Silence! Ye mutineering squibs! When I was young I had a mother who taught me to save. Ye've never been taught, but by Davy Jones's trousers, I'm going to teach ye now! The money's in that box—and there it stays!

CREW: Down with him! Mutiny! Mutiny! We want our gold!

[*There is another rush. The* CAPTAIN *bangs down the lid of the box and jumps upon it. Drawing his cutlass, he parries their blows and finally drives them into a corner.*]

CAPTAIN: Ah, would ye! I'll larn ye to save! Down on your knees, every man jack o' ye! Bill, put that chest in my cabin, and if there's another word o' gold from any of ye, I'll have that man's share melted and poured down his throat!

BILL: Aye, aye, Cap'n.

[*He removes the chest, the* CAPTAIN *following with drawn cutlass. The* CREW *look mutinous when he has gone.*]

SNOOKS: We'll never see the gold again!

SLIMY: It's ours by right! What claim has he to it?

RAMROD: Kill the dog!

ALL: Aye, blood, blood!

SNOOKS: Who's going to kill him?

BLOODWINKLE: We must do it all together, boys!

CREW: That's it, all together.

SNOOKS: Aye, there's safety in numbers.

CREW: Mutiny! Mutiny!

SLIMY: Who'll be the new captain?

RAMROD: I'm the only man to lead you to victory!

BLOODWINKLE: That's a lie! It's my idea.

CREW [*Separately*]: Ramrod! Bloodwinkle!

PETE: Let the man whose weapon drinks first of the Captain's blood be our new leader.

CREW: Aye, that's it!

BLOODWINKLE: Then we're all decided—death to the Captain and the Mate!

CREW: Aye, aye, death to the Captain!

CREW [*Singing*]:

> For mutiny this crew declare,
> Stand by to man the capstan.
> Let ev'ry man his steel prepare,
> To slay our cruel Captain.
> And on his hilt let each man swear
> To mutilate the Captain.*

[*They execute a very fierce march which concludes with a dramatic tableau while they swear on their hilts. Then* SLIT-GIZZARD BILL *runs on.*]

BILL: Cavy, boys, here's the Cap'n!

[*The effect is magical. The* CREW *retreat to their corner and drop to their knees. Enter the* CAPTAIN.]

CAPTAIN: Ha! There's too much music on board my ship. I mistrust musical crews. Stand by, ye lubbers, for a court-martial of the prisoners! Bloodwinkle and Ramrod, produce the aforesaid. Jump to it, now, ye vile cutthroats!

[*There is immediate activity. The deck is cleared and a place prepared for the* CAPTAIN *and the* MATE *on one side, while the* CREW *group themselves solemnly around. The* SCOUTS *are marched in by* RAMROD *and* BLOODWINKLE.]

CREW [*Snarling*]: Blood!

CAPTAIN: Silence! Slit-Gizzard Bill, read the accusation.

BILL [*Adjusting his spectacles*]: "You are charged with loitering with intent to do injury to members of the noble profession of Bloodthirsty Buccaneers, and, furthermore, with the treasonable and slanderous offense of saying you didn't believe in pirates."

* Tune: "Let Erin Remember"

CREW: The plank! The thumbscrew! Keelhaul 'em!

CAPTAIN: Silence in court! Have the prisoners anything to say?

TOM: Only that we think you're the filthiest set of bounders we ever set eyes on!

BERT: And, if you think we're afraid of you, you're jolly well mistaken!

CAPTAIN: Silence in court! Are the prisoners guilty?

CREW: Aye!

CAPTAIN: You have had a fair trial. It only remains for me to pronounce the sentence.

SLIMY: Cut their ears off!

SNOOKS: Boil 'em in oil!

CREW: Blood! Blood!

CAPTAIN: My crew, you will observe, have very old-fashioned methods. It will be my duty on this happy occasion to devise a more refined and original form of torture.

BERT: If you weren't such a set of lawless villains, you'd give us a chance to fight it out.

CAPTAIN: Fighting, is it? Which man will you fight?

BERT: If I had a choice, you're the man I should most like to fight. [*The* CREW *are contorted with laughter.*]

CAPTAIN: Me? Do you know there isn't a buccaneer on the Seven Seas would dare blink an eyelid at me? Now then, Bill, who was it fought Morgan to a finish?

BILL: You, Cap'n.

CAPTAIN: And who was it did for Jim the Blood-Drinker?

BILL: You, Cap'n.

CAPTAIN: Aye, me, and many a score of others.

BERT: Of course, if you're afraid of me . . .

CAPTAIN: Afraid! Shiver me timbers and shatter me mizzen-tops! Afraid o' you! That's good, that is! Ho! Ho! Ho!

BERT: Will you fight?

CAPTAIN: Well, I'm blowed! Give him a sword! [*He draws his cutlass.*]

TOM: I'll see fair play—and if you do for Bert, you've got to settle with me!

CAPTAIN: Here's another of 'em! Give me a noggin o' rum! This is the best sport I've had for many a day.

[BERT *is provided with a cutlass and* TOM *takes out his watch. The* CAPTAIN *takes a deep draught of rum, and they set to.* BERT *has some narrow escapes before* TOM *calls time. The* CAPTAIN *drinks more rum than is good for him and the fight goes on. The rum begins to tell—the* CAPTAIN'S *wind fails— and soon he is at* BERT'S *feet. The* CREW *cheer* BERT *as he places his foot on the* CAPTAIN'S *neck.*]

CAPTAIN [*Gasping*]: Ha! Vile brat, thou hast pinked me amidships! Shame, shame, what bitterness in thy sting! Captain Cutlass, thou art frazzled by an impertinent tadpole! I— ah—

BERT: Victory! Put him in chains and remove him to the jail cell!

TOM: Well done, Bert! [*They shake hands.*] And understand this, you ruffians! Bert's the Captain now! Salute him everybody!

[*The* CREW *salute and sing to their previous tune.*]

CREW [*Singing*]:
> Let cruel captains all beware—
> Three cheers for Captain Bertie!
> He's beat this man in battle fair,
> He scorns tricks mean and dirty;
> So on his hilt let each man swear
> To stand by Captain Bertie. [*Three cheers.*]

TOM: And I'm his mate. What orders, Captain?

BERT: Turn the ship and steer a straight course for England.

BILL: There ye are! Ye've been done! We're all for Execution Dock now!

BERT: Quite wrong, Mr. Slit-Gizzard William. We're for England, Home and Beauty, and, if you land in Execution

Dock, it's your own silly fault.

CREW: Bravo!

BERT: And, mind you, I'm Captain here now, and if I have any more of your mutinous back-chat, it'll be Execution Dock and no mistake!

A VOICE: Sail ho! [*The* CREW *rush to the side.*]

BILL: A sail on the port bow, Cap'n. Merchantman, by the look of her. Shall I put a shot across her bows?

BERT: Load the gun.

BILL: Aye, aye, Cap'n. [*The* CREW *load the gun.*]

TOM: I say, Bert, we can't board her. We aren't pirates really, you know.

BERT: That's just the trouble, Tom. But I've got to humor these scoundrels or we shan't have a ghost of a chance.

TOM: Let's fight the lot!

BERT: That's absurd. But I've got another plan. Haul down that Black Flag.

TOM: Aye, aye, Cap'n! [TOM *hauls down the Black Flag.*]

BILL: Now then! Hands off the flag!

BERT: My orders!

RAMROD: But we can't fight without a flag!

BERT: My orders, ye mutinous skunks! Listen to me!

TOM: Silence between decks, there!

BERT: Now then, you men, I'm a Scout, and while I'm Captain here, there's one Scout law that I mean to have obeyed, and it's this, every Scout must promise to do one good turn a day. Now you've all got neckerchiefs, and to remind you of that law I command every one of you to tie a knot in his neckerchief.

TOM: All hands tie knots in their neckerchiefs! Jump to it! [*The hands obey.*]

BERT: That's right. Now we'll start today well. For our first good turn, I intend to let that ship go by without looting her.

CREW [*Growling*]: Bah! Blood! We want blood!

BERT: Stop that noise!

TOM: Silence! Play the game, can't you?

BILL: We've been done, lads!

RAMROD: Chuck 'em overboard!

BLOODWINKLE: Down with the swine!

[*The* CREW *make an ugly movement forward, growling.*]

TOM: Stand back, you hounds! [*The* CREW *creep nearer.*]

BERT: My orders are the only orders on this ship. Get back to your posts!

SNOOKS: But don't you see, guv., if we does good turns, we ain't pirates, and if we ain't pirates, we loses our jobs.

CREW [*Ominously*]: Blood! Blood!

[TOM *drags the keg forward.* BERT *picks up a pistol.*]

BERT: Now, look here, my lads, we'd better understand one another. I'm a Scout, and I stand for King, Country and the Law. This ship's going to be respectable.

CREW [*Snarling*]: Ah! Blood! We want blood! [*They advance nearer.*]

BERT: Stop! Another step forward and I fire into this powder-keg and blow us all to smithereens! [*There is a sudden darkness, the* CREW *give a bloodcurdling howl, and . . .*]

Curtain

Scene III

SCENE—*The quay-side again. The same barrel (which looks suspiciously like a powder-keg), and the same* SCOUTS *asleep against it. A* POLICEMAN *enters, flashing his light about. He discovers the* SCOUTS *and rouses them in the manner of* SLIT-GIZZARD BILL.

POLICEMAN: Hey there! Wake up! Wake up, can't you!

BERT [*Rubbing his eyes and yawning*]: O-oh! Wake up, Tom! [*Suddenly jumping up.*] Stand back, you mutinous lubbers, or I'll let daylight into you!

TOM [*Wakening*]: Silence between decks! [BERT *attacks*

the POLICEMAN *with his pole*.]

POLICEMAN: Now, now, steady on! What's the little game?

BERT: What—why—I thought you were a pirate!

TOM: I say, what's happened?

BERT: Aren't you a pirate?

POLICEMAN: Look here, my lad, none of your sauce! I ain't a pirate and never was. I'm a police officer.

BERT: Sorry, but . . .

POLICEMAN: And so you ought to be—calling a respectable man names of that sort. Ought to be ashamed of yourself. Me a pirate! Cheek!

TOM: I say, have we been dreaming?

BERT: Of course we haven't been dreaming.

POLICEMAN: What I want to know is, what are you two doing asleep out here at this time of night? I've a good mind to charge you for it, in addition to the charge of assaulting the police in the execution of their duty.

BERT: You've been neglecting your duty. Do you know this place is swarming with pirates?

TOM: They carried us on board their ship—and if it hadn't been for Bert, they'd have murdered us!

POLICEMAN: Eh? Pirates?

BERT: Perhaps you're one of those people who don't believe in pirates.

POLICEMAN: Well, I'm blowed! [*He guffaws loudly*.]

TOM: It's no laughing matter, is it, Bert?

BERT [*Shaken by the* POLICEMAN'S *laugh*]: I—I don't know. I can't tell whether we dreamed it and we're awake now, or whether we were awake then and dreaming now. It's all so strange.

POLICEMAN: Ho! Ho! You've been dreaming. Look at me. You must be awake. *Nobody dreams policemen.*

TOM: Well, I'm jolly glad to be out of it. That was a tight corner.

POLICEMAN: There was a time when I believed in pirates.

TOM: Oh, but there are . . . unless . . .

[*The pirates' song is heard in the distance. It is the one about mutiny, and there is a kind of plaintive sadness in it, as though they are demanding their right to be believed in.*]

TOM: There you are! Listen!

BERT: The pirates' song!

POLICEMAN: I can't hear anything.

[*All three put their hands to their ears in strained attitudes— the* SCOUTS *thrilled, the* POLICEMAN *determined to investigate this business.*]

BERT: Listen, it's very faint.

TOM [*Beating time*]: It goes like this.

POLICEMAN: No, it's no good. [*He chokes down a sob.*]

BERT: You aren't deaf, are you?

POLICEMAN [*Weeping*]: I tell you it's no good. I can't hear them. There was a time when I heard them as plain as you, but the time's gone now. It's Annie Domino with me.

TOM: We're awfully sorry. We didn't know you had that.

POLICEMAN: Oh, it ain't a disease, it's just old age creeping on.

BERT: Ssh! They're going away.

POLICEMAN: I'm old and out of tune, that's what it is. I'd give a lot to hear them singing again. Don't you ever get old if you want to believe in pirates. Now then, my lads, come along home. They won't believe you there any more than I will, so you'd best look lively.

TOM: Are you coming, Bert?

BERT: I suppose so. I was just wondering whether I fired that pistol into the powder-barrel.

TOM: It's very queer—I feel more awake every minute.

BERT: But it seems to me that, if you only dream hard enough, it's as good as being awake.

TOM: Is that a new theory?

BERT: Oh, I don't know. [*Yawns.*] I feel horribly . . .

TOM: What? Sleepy?

BERT: No, awake. Let's go home.

Curtain

PRODUCTION NOTES

Tom and *Bert* are Boy Scouts who are much too wise to believe in pirates—until they make the acquaintance of *Captain Cutlass* and *Slit-Gizzard Bill*. Both boys have plenty of courage, however, to hold their own against a whole ship full of pirates. The boys have evidently been fishing at the time they are taken prisoners, for they have their poles with them. *Tom* carries a watch. He should be responsible for providing the black flag in the second scene, for he is the person who handles it. *Bert* must provide himself with a pistol, which he pretends to pick up from the deck in Scene II.

Captain Cutlass is a big, blustering pirate captain who puts terror into the hearts of all his bloodthirsty buccaneers. He calls them vile names, points his pistol and brandishes his cutlass at them, until he has them all cowering. A good, loud voice and a dominating personality are essential qualifications for the part. The boy who plays it must bellow forth his commands, and he must strut around the stage like a turkey-cock. He will need to provide himself with a lantern or a flashlight, a whistle, a pistol and a cutlass.

Bill, the mate, is not so easily cowed as are the other members of the crew, but even he steps quickly when the captain speaks. *Bill* carries a knife in his belt, and he takes from his pocket a pair of spectacles when he reads the accusation against *Tom* and *Bert.* (A pair of large sun glasses will make a good showing.) He should be responsible for providing a big box that can serve as a treasure chest.

The crew are a desperate-looking lot. Tousled hair and black mustaches made with an eyebrow pencil will completely alter the appearance of the most respectable-looking boy. If the crew will go without coats and wear a strip of bright-colored cloth around their waists and a triangular scarf around their necks, they will look sufficiently bloodthirsty to satisfy any audience. Each should wear a cap and carry a knife. Some one member of the crew— *Ramrod*, for example—should be made responsible for supplying a package of paper cups to serve as noggins for the rum. When the captain calls for rum, *Ramrod* is then the one to serve it. *Snooks* should have a fiddle or some other musical instrument which he plays for the dance at the opening of Scene II. Another member of the crew must be appointed in advance to do the dancing. Here is a good opportunity for an amateur tap dancer.

The policeman in Scene III will need a flashlight. A black rubber raincoat and hat will make a good uniform.

Merry Tyll

BY M. JAGENDORF

Characters

MARGUERITE, *who sells toys*

TYLL ULENSPIEGEL, *a merry prankster*

NELE, *who loves Tyll*

GILES, *who sells apples and gingerbread*

LOUIS, *a boy*

KATHELINE, *a girl*

SISKA, *her sister*

YAN, *a soldier*

JOSEPHUS, *a scholar*

COUNT HUGO

EGMONT, *his friend*

FRANÇOIS

PIERRE

BOYS, GIRLS, MONKS, NUNS, POOR AND RICH PEOPLE, SOLDIERS, ETC.

MERRY TYLL

Tyll Ulenspiegel is a legendary character of Germany and Flanders. He is one of the funniest and most nimble-witted rascals and pranksters known to legend and tradition. Tyll plays his jokes on his enemies but is always kind and helpful to the poor and the good people with whom he comes in contact.

One child who read the book, *Tyll Ulenspiegel's Merry Pranks* by M. Jagendorf, wrote: "Tyll was a man that believed in laughter and merry pranks and this book is certainly full of them."

Several of these stories tell of pranks which children like to dramatize.

The play, *Merry Tyll,* is best suited for production by the older children.

A market scene in the town of Bruges, late in the afternoon. There are but few people on the stage, for apparently there is some big attraction that is keeping them in another part of the square. Every now and then handclapping is heard off stage and shouts of "Hurrah!"

Three booths can be seen by the audience; one in the center of the stage and one on each side.

The first, to the right, is occupied by Marguerite, a young girl who sells toys and dolls. She sits in front of her booth. Next to her is the basket in which lie all sorts of toys. In the center of the stage is Tyll's booth, which looks somewhat like a marionette theater. Halfway down is a little cur-

tain. In front of his stand is a big square box (or barrel), to keep the audience from getting too close to him. Tyll and Nele sit quietly in front of the box, holding hands. To the left is Giles's booth. Giles is sitting in front with a basketful of apples and gingerbread. He has only one good eye, having lost the sight in the other when but a child. The latter is covered with a black patch. A stick lying in front of him indicates that he limps as well. He munches an apple.

LOUIS [*Running in out of breath*]: Where are they? Where are they?

GILES: Apples! Here are fine apples. Red apples! Oh, what ginger cakes—all covered with sweet honey! Buy an apple and a ginger cake and eat them together. It's Paradise food! Paradise food!

[*He pauses at intervals and thumps the ground with his stick.*]
[*Enter* KATHELINE *and* SISKA. KATHELINE *is pulling her sister by the hand, for* SISKA *is much younger and cannot walk so fast.*]

KATHELINE: Faster, Siska, faster, or we'll miss the play of the clowns.

SISKA [*Almost weeping*]: I cannot, Sister; I cannot run any faster.

MARGUERITE: Here, little girls, here are fine carved toys. Toys fit for little princesses. Dolls that can dance and horses that can prance. Come, buy a lovely doll.

KATHELINE [*Stopping*]: I like your toys, but I want to see the clowns.

[*Shouts and laughter are heard from outside. The two children run out.*]

MARGUERITE: I wish the clowns were a thousand leagues from here. I've hardly sold a doll all afternoon.

TYLL [*Laughing full-throatedly*]: If you had, you'd have one lovely doll less. Oh, wouldn't she, Nele?

[NELE *moves closer to him and does not answer.*]

MARGUERITE: A pox on your jesting! I'm tired of it.

GILES: Nay, say not that, Marguerite. 'Tis not Tyll's fault that we don't sell our wares. 'Twould be much worse without his merry, merry wit.

TYLL: Nele.

NELE: Ay, Tyll.

TYLL: See, there is someone coming. [*He points to the left. She turns around, and he kisses her quickly on the opposite cheek.*]

NELE [*Blushing*]: Tyll—someone might look.

TYLL: And what if they did? [*Still laughing.*] I love you, and I fear not if any one knows it. Hey, Giles, you know I love Nele.

GILES [*Laughing*]: I know full well.

TYLL: Look, sweet Nele, he knows I love you and he lives natheless.

[*A great shouting and handclapping are heard from the crowd without. Many children and a few grown-ups come in, in groups, talking.* NELE *quickly jumps up.* TYLL *does the same, getting behind the box in front of the curtain.* MARGUERITE *pushes her basket forward.*]

TYLL [*In singsong voice*]: Come little, come big. Come one and all. Come hither and have your fortunes told. Come here and learn your past, present and future.

MARGUERITE: Toys! Fine toys! Lovely dolls!

GILES: Apples! Gingerbreads shaped like saints and sweet as their deeds.

VOICES IN THE CROWD: That was a rare sight. Did you see the bear? The clowns flying through the air! And the gypsies dancing! I wish they'd do it again. I never saw the like.

GILES: Here are wonders! Fine apples!

MARGUERITE: Princess' toys! Countess' toys! Knights' horses that prance; toys that dance.

FROM THE CROWD: I'd give a deal to know how these clowns can do such marvelous tricks. 'Twas the strangest sight

I ever saw.

TYLL: Not as strange as what I have to show you. [*Drawing the curtain and displaying an empty straw frame hanging on a string.*] Look at this straw frame. Here, come here. Here in this selfsame frame you'll see the most marvelous show on earth. Here you can see your true selves. As you were, as you will be. One penny; only a single penny and you can learn your future! I'll teach you how to gain good fortune!

GILES: Aye, that he can, Tyll Ulenspiegel.

TYLL: True—all that for one penny. Come here, all. Come learn your weal—learn your woe. Come, come . . .

[*The crowd has gathered around the box. A* SOLDIER *pushes forward from the crowd.*]

SOLDIER YAN: Come, you with the ass's ear, tell me my fortune.

TYLL: That I will right gladly, bloated iron-eater. But first a penny.

ONE IN THE CROWD: First pay.

SOLDIER YAN [*Throwing down a coin*]: Here, loud blabber-mouth, and woe betide you if you don't give me a good fortune.

TYLL: That I will, sword swallower. Come closer to the box so I can look at you. Here's your fortune.

[*He jumps behind the screen, bends down and rummages for a moment underneath, then brings up a platter in which are bits of meat and moldy bread. He sticks the platter through the straw frame.*]

SOLDIER YAN: Quick, speak up.

TYLL: You'll learn soon enough, great conqueror of valiant men, what's in store for you. Look, here is your fortune. See this platter which is set in my strawen frame. You'll see therein bits of rotting meat and moldy bread crumbs. That, Master Soldier, will be your fortune to come. Great wars will make mincemeat of your muscles and moldy green crust of your brains. 'Twas well worth a penny to learn this future, wasn't it, soldier? Pay more and I'll tell you more.

SOLDIER YAN [*In a fury*]: Pay more, you scurvy imp? I've a good mind to hack you to pieces.

TYLL: Oho, great warrior! 'Tis not necessary to show your valor against me. [*To the crowd.*] What say you, good friends?

THE CROWD [*Jeering*]: Fie! I'd be ashamed to hit a little fellow. Look at the hero! It's a poor man who can't stand the truth from Merry Tyll.

[*The* SOLDIER *goes off quickly, muttering.*]

NELE: Tyll, Tyll, have a care for my sake. The next might carry out his threat.

TYLL: I fear no man or beast, leastways a braggart.

[*Enter* COUNT HUGO *and his friend* EGMONT. *They are, of course, dressed much finer than those present, and each carries a sword.*]

COUNT HUGO: And what have we here?

TYLL: Who is next? Who is the next to learn their fortune? Come. All for but a single penny. Ah, there I see a most scholarly face. I am certain, scholar, you'd like to learn if you'll be a great clerk or counselor some day? Ho, there, with the owl's face. I'll tell you such fortune as was never told before.

[*The tall, thin, scholarly-looking boy is not over-anxious to come up, but the crowd jostles him right to the box.*]

FROM THE CROWD: Tell him a scholarly fortune, Tyll. He has a face from which I am certain any fortune would run.

TYLL: I'll stop it from running and bring it right to him for but a single penny.

FROM THE CROWD: Come, out with your penny, Horned Spectacles. Don't be a miser. Match your wits against his, Tyll. He'll tell you a great fortune.

TYLL: That I will. Now a penny.

[*The crowd mills around the* SCHOLAR, *urging him ahead. He is very reluctant and moves only when pushed.*]

[*The director will be able to time this scene properly without any difficulty.*]

EGMONT: I wager a silver buckle you don't.

COUNT HUGO: The buckle is mine. Watch.

[*The crowd is still all around* TYLL, *urging the* SCHOLAR *on. He finally takes out his penny and gives it to* TYLL. *During the ensuing speech of* TYLL'S, COUNT HUGO *slowly works his way to where* NELE *stands.*]

TYLL: Master with the face of knowledgeable importance, would you learn your past, present and future? It's a simple thing. [*He puts his own face inside the frame and commences to cut grimaces.*]

TYLL [*Continuing*]: Look, saucer-eyes! My grimaces are the mirror, they tell the dullness and sourness of your mind. Your countenance foretells years of dust and dry parchment. Take care, else you will soon be hid in a dark shelf for centuries to come, even as the documents over which you pore— [HUGO *has by then come very close to* NELE, *who is standing aside, watching the scene with a somewhat detached look. When he is right next to her, he quickly kisses her on the cheek.* NELE, *feeling his lips on her cheek, screams and gives him a buffet on the nose.* TYLL *leaps from behind the booth and with one bound is next to* NELE.]

TYLL: Who harmed you, Nele? [*His eyes flash, and the fool's cap has fallen from his forehead.*]

NELE [*Pointing to* HUGO]: That fellow there.

HUGO: And what if I did? Since when are peasant wrenches so squeamish when a noble deigns to look at them?

TYLL: When dogs snap you kick 'em, even if they have fine fur. You common lout! Where did you steal that dagger? No real noble would so attack a maid. Put up your fists and I'll send you flying to pick your teeth in the gutter.

HUGO: I am a noble and don't fight with common mountebanks.

TYLL: O, messire, I forgot. True, you can ill afford to soil your milk face with my good fists. I'd—

EGMONT: Come, let us go, Count Hugo. The air is too full of sweat and garlic.

TYLL: Why so soon, masters? How would you, messire, like three kisses from her whom you tried to rob of one, eh? Hey, there, Nele, you'll give this noble gentleman three kisses—

NELE: That I'll not.

TYLL: Oh, yes, you will!

EGMONT: Come, Count, let us go.

TYLL: Oh, no, don't! If three kisses are not enough, then she'll give each three.

NELE: Tyll, for shame!

FROM THE CROWD: What's the game, Tyll? He is up to some trick.

TYLL: No tricks at all. They can each have three kisses from Nele, for certain; but there is one condition. Listen, noble scions! You'll not fight a clown with sword nor fists—such is the wont and custom. But it is customary for noble to match his wit against clowns. Surely you who have been brought up with fine books of learning will answer three questions which I'll put to you. If either of you succeed, you can both have three kisses from this lovely maid.

HUGO [*Who is now surrounded by the crowd and finds it difficult to get out*]: What do you mean?

TYLL: You'd not fight me with rapier or fist!

HUGO [*With contempt*]: Nobles don't fight clowns.

TYLL: Quite true, but as I said before, it is the wont and custom for noble to match his wit against jester.

FROM THE CROWD: Aye, such is the custom. Naught has ever been said against that. Take care, Tyll has a clever tongue. He is renowned for the nimbleness of his mind.

EGMONT: Come, Count, let us go.

TYLL: Oh, no! . . . Why go when there is sport on hand? Surely a noble count's son won't run from matching his learned mind against a dull clown. Six kisses if you win, a golden ducat for me if you lose; and all for answering three questions I'll put to you.

NELE: How dare you, Tyll! [TYLL *silences her with a knowing look.*]

FROM THE CROWD: That's fair. That's fair.

COUNT HUGO: I'll take your challenge.

FROM THE CROWD: Now for a rare spectacle. Come, Tyll, show if you deserve the credit for a nimble wit.

TYLL: Messire Count, this is our wager. I will give you three questions and if either of you answer them correctly, six kisses from Nele; if you fail, I receive a ducat.

NELE: Tyll—

TYLL: Nele, it has not yet come to pass.

HUGO: I am ready.

EGMONT: Perhaps they are questions none can answer.

TYLL: I'll answer each and every one of them.

HUGO: I can answer aught a clown can answer.

TYLL: Welladay. First, Messire Count Hugo, tell me how many bits of straw are there in this my straw frame which helps me tell fortunes? [*He holds the frame close to him.*]

HUGO: How am I to know how many straws there are in your dirty straw frame?

TYLL: I know. One thousand nine hundred and eighty-seven.

EGMONT: How do we know you speak the truth?

TYLL: Deny it if you can. If you don't believe me, sit down and count them right here.

FROM THE CROWD [*Great commotion*]: Tyll told the truth. Either sit down and count them or take his word for it. That was a clever one.

TYLL: Now, Messire Count, you have a learned master to teach you the great truths of the world, wherefore it should be a simple matter for you to tell me quickly where is the center of the earth.

EGMONT: None knows that.

COUNT HUGO [*Sarcastically*]: Perhaps you with the ass's ears can tell that.

TYLL: I can full well. The center of the earth, O noble monument of learning, is right where you stand. Measure it to the right and to the left and you will see I am telling the truth. I measured it three moons ago.

FROM THE CROWD: Tyll tells the truth. If you don't believe, measure it!

TYLL: Now for the third question. What, O noble fellow, will happen to you this Saturday ten years from today?

COUNT HUGO: How am I to know?

TYLL: I know. You'll have a full growth of ass's ears on your forehead, and instead of talking, you'll bray like a donkey.

FROM THE CROWD [*Jubilantly*]: Hurray! Tyll! Tyll has won. None can dispute him.

TYLL: You have not answered a single question. I did, therefore you owe me a ducat.

EGMONT: They were not fair.

TYLL: I could answer them. Now, my merry little noble fellows, pay.

HUGO [*Taking out a gold coin and flinging it to him*]: There is your ducat.

[*From afar, the ringing of a church bell is heard.*]

TYLL: There is the bell. Good day, messires. You had best go, or you'll miss your dainty supper. Good cheer to you, and remember, I think I have well proven that the ass's ears on my fool's cap are only sewn, whereas they are commencing to show in full growth on your foreheads.

[*There is laughter from the crowd.*]

HUGO [*Full of anger*]: Laugh, lout, laugh! But beware. 'Tis not the last word yet. [*Darkly and slowly.*] I'll return soon enough and pay you back in good coin.

TYLL: Whenever you return, I'll be right ready to receive you in due and proper form. [*With a grand bow.*] Pray let it be right soon.

HUGO: It'll be soon enough.

[HUGO *and* EGMONT *leave with ugly and threatening expressions on their faces.*]

FROM THE CROWD: Good riddance. Well done, Tyll. 'Twas a fine sight to see you throw the noble off his high perch. You will be a jester some day at a king's court.

[*As they speak they bid him good-by and gradually disappear. Soon, only* TYLL, NELE, GILES *and* MARGUERITE *are left.* MARGUERITE *is packing her toys, getting ready to leave. Twilight has set in.*]

NELE: Oh, Tyll, how proud I am of you! Yet I am sore afeared they will do you some harm yet.

TYLL: They can't harm me. I have an iron armor of wit and they can't come nigh it within seven leagues.

MARGUERITE: You had better take care, Tyll. They can't come nigh you with brains, but they can easily reach you with cudgels. Have a care, Tyll. A merry good night to both of you. Ah! but 'twas a fine trick [*laughs*], and clever. Good night.

TYLL: ⎤
          ⎬ Good night, Marguerite. Good night.
NELE: ⎦

NELE: You must be famished, Tyll.

TYLL [*Busying himself with putting his things together*]: Nele, you are a greater magician than I am, for you guess real truths. I am so hungry I could eat you and a big meal besides. But I must wait here for Father to pass. He is bringing victuals from the mart and I must help him carry them home.

GILES: Here are apples and gingerbread. 'Twas well worth the sport you furnished me. [*He throws them the apples and the gingerbread, which they catch dexterously.*]

TYLL: Come, Nele, everything is now put away securely. Let us sit here and while the time away in a manner I like best until my father comes.

[*They both sit down on the ground against the box which stands in front of the booth. They sit quite close.*]

NELE: Tyll, you are a wild fellow.

TYLL: Would you have me sad and ever silent? [*She does not answer but moves closer to him. It is getting darker.*] So, that is better. Come still closer. [*He puts his arms around her.*]

NELE: Don't, Tyll. Someone might see.

TYLL: All are gone save Giles, and he has but one eye and therefore sees but half of what we are doing.

NELE: Stop mocking. I love Giles, even if he has but a single eye.

TYLL: And I do, too; wherefore we need not mind him at all. I've heard a new song, Nele. Come still closer, and I'll sing it to you.

> Come to me, O come! *
> Let me die, but come!
>> Hyria hysria nazaza
>> Trillirivos.
>
> Fair is thy face, O fair!
> Fair thine eyes, O how fair!
>> Hyria hysria nazaza
>> Trillirivos.
>
> Fair is thy flowing hair!
> O fair, how fair, how fair!
>> Hyria hysria nazaza
>> Trillirivos.
>
> Fairer than all I vow
> Ever my pride art thou
>> Hyria hysria nazaza
>> Trillirivos.

How do you like the song, Nele?

NELE: I love you, Tyll. If only you'd not be ever courting

* This is one of the rustic melodies included in John Addington Symond's collection of medieval songs, *Wine, Woman and Song,* published by Mc-Clure, Phillips & Co. Tune: First eight bars "Gilone and Gillette," *Pantomimes for the Children's Theater* (p. 6). New York. Brentano's.

quarrels. I am sore afeared for you.

[*From afar there is the sounding of a bell.*]

TYLL: It ill becomes a sweetheart of mine to speak of fear. Fear! I know not what it is. There is naught in the world I fear, not—Sh-h! What's that? Listen! [*Voices are heard outside.*] It's Count Hugo. Quick, Nele, they are coming this way, and certes for no good reason. Giles!

GILES [*Who has dozed off, waking*]: Aye, Tyll.

TYLL: Let Nele sit with you so she can't be seen. I'll hide in the box. Use your wits well, if Count Hugo asks you about me. Tell him I am gone, but may soon return.

NELE: Tyll—

TYLL: Quick—they are here. Do as I bid.

[*He bustles her over to* GILES'S *booth, and she sits back in the shadow so that she is not seen. He hides in the box which stands in front of the booth. Enter* COUNT HUGO, EGMONT *and two unkempt-looking fellows,* FRANÇOIS *and* PIERRE.]

FRANÇOIS: We both know Tyll Ulenspiegel well.

PIERRE: Who doesn't? There is his fortune-telling booth.

HUGO: That is the place where that lout, that mangy clown, plies his trade.

EGMONT: It's him we mean. If you make him look so his own mother won't recognize him, there is a golden ducat for each.

HUGO: He may come back later. Let us ask that one-eyed apple cheater. [*To* GILES.] Ho, there, you, is Tyll Ulenspiegel coming back this evening?

[TYLL *quickly pops his head from behind the box, nodding vigorously to indicate to* GILES *to say yes.* GILES *sees it; the others, of course, do not, for their backs are turned to the box.*]

GILES: That he is—soon.

FRANÇOIS: Good. We'll earn the ducats this evening yet. When we are through with him, he'll not look like a human.

EGMONT: Bide your time and set upon him as soon as he

arrives.

PIERRE: Never fear, we'll take care. Ho, ho, ho, I can feel the ducat in my pouch!

HUGO: I want him so beaten up that he'll not be able to walk for months. Don't forget there is a golden ducat for each.

FRANÇOIS: It'll be worth more'n a ducat.

TYLL [*Popping his head out for a moment*]: Ho, ho! [GILES *also laughs.*]

EGMONT: What was that? [*They all listen.*]

FRANÇOIS: Naught save that one-eyed thief with the apples, laughing. You there, stop that, or it'll not go well with you.

EGMONT: We'll go now and return later, when your task is done. It's then you'll be paid.

FRANÇOIS: We'll do our work well.

[EGMONT *and* HUGO *leave.* FRANÇOIS *and* PIERRE *sit down against the box where, just a little while ago,* TYLL *and* NELE *sat. The stage is now quite dark. In the distance, the bell still rings every now and then. Someone is also playing a flute.**]

FRANÇOIS: I wonder how long Tyll will be in coming.

PIERRE: Ho, there, you with the single eye. You said he'd return soon, didn't you?

GILES: Soon enough. He'll be here right soon.

[TYLL *carefully puts out a hand and gives a violent tug at* FRANÇOIS' *hair, withdrawing on the instant.*]

FRANÇOIS [*Turning quickly to* PIERRE]: What do you mean by pulling my hair, you filthy sow?

PIERRE: Don't you call me filthy sow. I did not pull your hair. I don't seek vermin in thieves' skulls.

FRANÇOIS: If you say another word, I'll pound the breath out of your chest.

PIERRE: Try and do it.

[*They sit silent for a few seconds.* TYLL *carefully puts out his hand and whacks* PIERRE *soundly on his back.*]

---

* Any instrument, like a guitar or mandolin or violin, might be used instead.

PIERRE [*Leaping up*]: What the fiends has got into you? Why beat me? You yapping cur! If you do this again, I'll thwack your hide until it looks like dried parchment.

FRANÇOIS: I never beat you. I've been sitting here quietly, never raising my hand, just wondering how much longer we must wait for that lout.

PIERRE: You lie. You beat me because you said that I pulled your hair. Where is that accursed clown?

GILES: Not far. Not far.

PIERRE: A curse on him! I'd wish he'd come. I am just in fine fettle to play drums on his head and neck.

[*He sits down. No sooner has he done so than* TYLL *puts out his hands steathily and gives a violent pull at* PIERRE'S *hair and at the same time delivers an ugly blow at* FRANÇOIS'S *head, so that he almost falls over. Both leap up.*]

FRANÇOIS: You hound—you hit—

PIERRE: You mongrel—you pulled out a handful of my hair.

[*They stand ready to fly at each other.*]

FRANÇOIS: I never did, you spittle of the devil.

PIERRE: I never did, you blear-eyed hound—

FRANÇOIS: You lie. . . .

[*They are so engrossed in each other that they don't notice* TYLL *stealing out from under the box, giving a sound kick to* FRANÇOIS' *shin. At that* FRANÇOIS, *without another word, leaps upon* PIERRE *and commences to beat and kick him.* PIERRE *returns the fare with double interest. They thwack and beat each other, rolling around on the floor.* GILES *is doubling up with laughter.* TYLL *runs over to* NELE *and takes hold of her arm.*]

TYLL: Come quick, sweetheart. I've served these two their proper fare—ho, ho, ho! And 'twas Tyll they were going to beat black and blue.

[*The two on the ground stop, exhausted, and first notice* TYLL. *They both look at him with eyes wide open.*]

FRANÇOIS: ⎫
PIERRE: ⎭ What—ho—

TYLL: My guiding angel set you upon each other as a punishment for wanting to beat me. He directed your fists right and proper. A merry good night.

[*He is off quickly with* NELE. *The two leap up from the ground to go after him, but the entrance of* HUGO *and* EGMONT *arrests them.*]

HUGO: I heard the noise of quarrel and blows. Did you beat that accursed hound as you promised to?

[*Neither* FRANÇOIS *nor* PIERRE *replies.*]

EGMONT: You look as if you'd gone through a great battle.

PIERRE: Aye, we did.

HUGO: Where is that lout?

FRANÇOIS: Gone.

HUGO: Gone? How?

FRANÇOIS [*Speaking hurriedly*]: He ran. We beat him up so terrible his best friends won't recognize him. He gave us a great battle, though.

PIERRE [*Grimly*]: That he surely did.

COUNT HUGO: Fine. Fine indeed.

FRANÇOIS: We certes earned our money.

PIERRE [*Catching on to* FRANÇOIS]: That we did. He made us fight like wild cats. Look at our clothes. We gave it to him, though.

COUNT HUGO [*Taking out money and giving it to them*]: Here.

FRANÇOIS: Thanks, Master Count. I hope we can serve you soon again.

[*From the distance,* TYLL *and* NELE'S *voices can be heard singing.*]

TYLL *and* NELE:

> Fairer than all I vow
> Ever my pride art thou
>   Hyria hysria nazaza. . . .

HUGO: 'Tis he, Tyll singing. How's that?

GILES [*Rising to go with his basket*]: Aye, 'tis he. Such is ever his wont, Messires—to be merry, no matter what comes to pass.

EGMONT [*To* FRANÇOIS *and* PIERRE]: It seems to me, judging from your appearances, 'twas you got the beating and not Tyll.

PIERRE [*Ugly*]: No matter what happened, we earned our money.

GILES: That they did full well, Messire Count. You forgot no harm can ever come to Tyll, for his greatest joy is to right the wrong and sing his way through life.

[*He goes out laughing while the four remaining look at one another angrily.*]

PRODUCTION NOTES

Characters: Four girls, nine boys, mob. Ages ranging from six to sixteen. Many boys' parts are interchangeable.

Time of action: About forty-five minutes.

Scenery: Three sets of screens. Left: white background, red outline of house; blue sky over left-hand panel; yellow house, black window. Center screen: yellow ground color; red poles and ornaments; white painted box for stand, red ornaments. Alongside of this, jutting out to the side, must stand a large box or barrel behind which Tyll hides toward the end of the play. End screen: white ground color; green windows; blue skyline on right panel; red outline of house; black windows.

Instead of design indicated, some medieval scene might be copied. Consult any history volume with colored drawings.

Costumes:

Marguerite: dark green shawl or cape; yellow dress; black or white apron.

Tyll: Red buckram, paper, or stocking cap and ears; white muslin ruff; white shirt; black sateen vest; red sateen trousers.

Nele: Black sateen vest; red and white striped skirt; green stockings; black slippers, red hat.

Giles: Ragged gray flannel cloak; green and white striped stocking cap; ragged trousers.

François and Pierre: Red flannel cap and cloak; gray sateen trousers; black shoes. The color of the materials of each might be varied.

Count Hugo: Black skull-cap, with gold cardboard or material ornaments and green sateen rim; black velvet neckcloth; green sateen gown; black velvet trimmings on gown and sleeves. Black stockings; red felt shoes; gold decorations.

Egmont: Somewhat similar or any medieval costume.

Soldier: Head gear of buckram or cardboard, painted silver; armor and boots. Gilded feather; silvered cardboard shield; red flannel jacket and trousers.

Crowd: Follow designs in any good medieval costume book.

Properties: Stick, basket with apples and gingerbread, real or artificial. Paint apples and gingerbread on cardboard; one real apple and gingerbread cake. Basket with dolls, real or painted on cardboard; large packing box or barrel; small curtain; platter with bits of bread and meat and bones; a straw frame large enough for Tyll to put his head through; either real straw or painted effect; bell, flute or violin, or mandolin; bell for Tyll's cap; wand for Tyll; copy from some medieval scene.

Lighting: Action runs during late afternoon, sunset and dark twilight. Adjust colors accordingly.

Music: The song should be accompanied by faint music from flute, mandolin, or any other string instrument. Any other old song may be used instead.

Note: Giles and Marguerite cry out their wares in singsong tones. Tyll addresses the crowd in the same manner. Instead of the costumes described, medieval design such as will be found in any good volume on the subject may be used.

How Boots Befooled the King

ADAPTED FROM HOWARD PYLE'S THE WONDER CLOCK

BY SOPHIE L. GOLDSMITH

Characters

KING

QUEEN

JESTER

FIRST SUITOR

SECOND SUITOR

HERALD

FATHER

PETER

PAUL

BOOTS

OLD CROCKERY VENDER

HIS DAUGHTER

LORD COUNCILOR

HIS DAUGHTER

COUNCILOR'S FIRST MAIDSERVANT

COUNCILOR'S SECOND MAIDSERVANT

FIRST LADY IN WAITING

SECOND LADY IN WAITING

PRINCESS'S NURSE

PRINCESS

HOW BOOTS BEFOOLED THE KING
From *Wonder Clock Plays*. Adapted from Howard Pyle's "The Wonder Clock," by Sophie L. Goldsmith. Copyright, 1925, Harper & Brothers. Copyright, 1953, Sophie L. Goldsmith.

HOW BOOTS BEFOOLED THE KING

How Boots Befooled the King and *The Staff and the Fiddle* are dramatizations of stories with the same titles in *The Wonder Clock* by Howard Pyle. The stories are based on old folklore sources and are closely related in plot and spirit to the actual folk tales. Pyle's own brand of humor and interpretation of plot, together with his fine powers of imagination, make these favorites with storytellers and children of all ages. It is one of the happiest and most humorous collections of tales retold that we have.

The illustrations in *The Wonder Clock* are by the author and they should be very helpful in planning the scenes, properties, costumes and stage requirements for the plays. There is nothing arbitrary about the costume suggestions to be found at the end of each play. They have been tried and proved successful, so they are included for what they may be worth.

Act I
Scene 1

The throne room of the palace. KING *and* QUEEN *on their thrones, with the* JESTER *at feet of* KING. *Throughout the play, the* JESTER *has barely a speaking part, but acts constantly—dancing, mimicking, talking to his bauble, etc.*

KING: Well, my dear, this has been a quiet day, thank heaven! Not a suitor here for the Princess.

QUEEN [*Going to window*]: Not so fast, Husband! The road

109

is crowded. At this very moment, a young man is knocking at the door, and others are jostling him hard.

KING: A plague on them! Will they leave me no peace?

QUEEN: Now, now, dear, keep cool! I'm sure I can't help it if she's so attractive, although [*simpering*] in a way it *is* my fault.

KING: No, no, I won't have you reproach yourself! It is my fault that she is so irresistible—all mine.

QUEEN: No, my love, *I* insist on taking the blame.

KING: Well, well, we'll try not to quarrel. [*Flourish of trumpet. Enter* HERALD.]

HERALD: Your Majesty, the Prince of Thingumbobbia solicits an audience with you.

KING: Show him in.

[HERALD *brings in* FIRST SUITOR.]

FIRST SUITOR: O, King, I have come to pay court to your daughter.

KING: Sing it again.

FIRST SUITOR: I said, I have come to pay court to your daughter. There is none like her, so goes the rumor, throughout the length and breadth of the land. I would have her for my bride.

QUEEN: And what have you done, to deserve such a treasure?

FIRST SUITOR: The six-headed dragon have I slain, O King!

KING: Proceed.

FIRST SUITOR: Also, I possess the cap of invisibility and the magic ring.

QUEEN: I implore you, King, do not listen to him! The house is already overrun with caps and rings, which are picturesque, but powerless.

KING [*Patting her hand reassuringly*]: Fear not, little one. [*To* FIRST SUITOR.] You do not interest me, sir. I already have a patent dragon-killer, and, as the Queen says, in the way of invisible caps and magic rings our interior decorations are complete.

FIRST SUITOR: But—

KING: Good day, sir!

FIRST SUITOR: Just allow me, sire—

KING: Away with you! [JESTER *ushers him out, mockingly.*]

QUEEN: I think you might be just a little bit gentler, dear.

KING: Pah! Must they be treated like women? If the Princess had been a man, I'd have been saved all this trouble, anyhow.

QUEEN: Are you again blaming me for that? Oh dear! oh dear! [*Starts to weep.*]

KING: There, there, my dear, don't take it so hard. You did your best, I know. [*Another knock.*] Is that another suitor? [*Enter* HERALD.]

HERALD: The Duke of Woddyecallem to see Your Majesty.

QUEEN [*Drying her eyes*]: Show him in.

[HERALD *ushers in* SECOND SUITOR.]

SECOND SUITOR: Good day, Your Majesty!

KING [*Impatiently*]: Well, well, well!

SECOND SUITOR: I have come—

KING: Yes, yes, be quick!

SECOND SUITOR: To ask your permission—

KING: Another one! Good heavens!

SECOND SUITOR: But do allow me to finish, Your Majesty! I only want leave to marry your lovely daughter.

QUEEN: *Only,* sir, *only!* You have a strange way of putting it.

SECOND SUITOR: That is true, madam. But see what I have to offer her!

KING: Well, what have you to offer her?

SECOND SUITOR [*Drawing near, confidentially*]: I have a magic horse which, if I but say Gurrumgorrroooo, will carry me wherever I wish.

QUEEN: I don't like that. I want my son-in-law to be a

home-loving man.

KING: What else have you?

SECOND SUITOR: I have a magic sword which kills all who fight against it.

KING: That's not a sporting proposition. I like to see a good scrap. What else have you?

SECOND SUITOR: I have a loaf of bread which never grows smaller. As soon as a piece is bitten off, there is another in its place.

QUEEN: Send him away, Your Majesty, send him away! Our daughter is quite lazy enough already! Why shouldn't she bake bread every day, I'd like to know?

KING: Yes, indeed! What else is the poor girl to do? Away with you, Duke Woddyecallem!

SECOND SUITOR: But—

KING: Away, I say! [DUKE *kneels.* JESTER *drives him out.*]

QUEEN: Well, I'm glad that's over. Magic loaf, indeed! Why, the Princess would certainly do nothing *but* loaf! Ha! Ha!

KING: It's all very well for you to joke and made bad puns, but I have no peace any more. These fellows will be the death of me.

QUEEN: My poor kingy-wingy!

KING: I tell you I am weary of it all! A pack of braggarts and imposters! None of them can fool *me!*

JESTER: Would you have one who *could* fool you, sire? Why not try me?

KING [*Gazes at him intently. Rises, strikes his forehead dramatically with his scepter*]: Not so bad, fool, not so bad! [JESTER *begins to hum* "Wedding March," *walking to altar, etc.*]

QUEEN: My liege! Not that person?

KING: Nonsense! Have I not listened to his fooleries these many years, without being taken in by them? [JESTER *collapses in mock despair.*] Herald! Come hither!

HERALD: I am hither, sire!

KING: Proclaim far and wide that only the man who can befool the King shall win his daughter. Those who fail shall be soundly beaten!

QUEEN: But, sire, have mercy! You, who are so penetrating, so wise, who can fool you?

KING: Proclaim it, Herald! Only the man who can befool the wisest King in the world may marry his daughter! Those who fail shall be soundly beaten!

QUEEN: Alas! Alas! She will die an old maid!

KING: Be still, woman! Herald, proclaim!

HERALD: Oyez! Oyez! Oyez! His Gracious Majesty King Wiseacres proclaims that only the man who can befool him shall marry the lovely Princess! Those who fail shall be soundly beaten! [*Walking to other side of stage.*] Oyez! Oyez! Oyez! His Gracious Majesty King Wiseacres proclaims that only the man who can befool him shall marry the lovely Princess! Those who fail shall be soundly beaten! [QUEEN *falls at feet of* KING, *begging for mercy.*]

Curtain

Act II
Scene 1

FATHER, PETER, PAUL *and* BOOTS *seated in their cottage, in front of a fireplace.* PETER *whittling,* PAUL *idle,* BOOTS *poking in ashes.* FATHER *smoking long pipe.*

FATHER: Did you hear the King's proclamation, boys?

PETER: Aye, that we did! And we mean to have a try for the Princess.

FATHER: Go, by all means. It would be fine to have a princess in the family.

PETER: I try first, for I am the oldest.

PAUL: And if he fails, I shall try my luck.

FATHER: Yes, indeed! For one of you two must surely be

able to befool the King, fine fellows that you are.

BOOTS: And if they fail, how about me?

PETER: You? *You?* But that is too droll! A stupid fellow like you!

PAUL: You, who do naught all day but poke in the ashes!

BOOTS: That's as it may be. If you fail, may I not have my turn?

FATHER: *If* they fail! Ha! Ha! That's a safe promise! Do you think you can succeed where they fail?

BOOTS: But I may try?

FATHER: Yes, you may try. And now hurry, get your brothers ready.

PETER: Hand me my plumed cap, stupid! So you think I go courting bareheaded?

PAUL: Don't you see I am waiting for my staff, idiot? And a handkerchief to dust off my shoes. Am I to appear before the Princess with dirty shoes?

BOOTS [*Bustling about as required*]: Yes, yes, dear brothers. Go, and good luck to you!

FATHER: Good luck! Good luck!

PETER: And you shall have your chance, Boots, if we fail!

PAUL: Yes, *if* we fail! Ha! Ha!

BOTH: Ha! Ha! [*Go out laughing,* BOOTS *and* FATHER *waving good-by.*]

    Curtain

    Scene 2

    Same as Act I. KING, QUEEN *and* JESTER *in throne room. Enter* HERALD.

HERALD: A suitor for the Princess, Your Majesty.

KING: Does he look promising?

HERALD: I cannot tell, Your Majesty. His name is Peter.

QUEEN: Peter! Peter! Rhymes with wife-beater. The sound of it likes me not!

KING: It sounds healthy to me. Show the fellow in!

HERALD [*Announcing*]: Master Peter!

[*Enter* PETER.]

PETER: Good day, Your Majesty. I have come to fool you.

KING: Thanks for the hint.

PETER: Of course, it isn't April Fools' Day, Your Majesty. You will pardon the liberty I take. You proclaimed it yourself.

KING: What an idiot! And you think *you* can fool *me*!

PETER: Yes, yes, Your Majesty. I know I can. Only look outside in the courtyard.

KING: Yes.

PETER: Do you not see? There are three black geese there. Ha! Ha! Ha! Three black geese, I said!

KING: I see only one goose right in this room, and in a moment he will be not only black, but black and blue. Off with you!

[JESTER *beats him out of the room with a small switch.*]

KING: Well, that's one, so far. Fool me indeed! *Me*!

HERALD: Another suitor for the Princess, Your Highness.

KING: What is his name?

HERALD: It is Paul, Your Majesty.

KING: Paul? Rhymes with fall. He'd better not come in.

QUEEN: Ah, give him a chance, Your Majesty. Suppose my father had treated you that way!

KING: True, true. Show him in.

HERALD [*Ushering in* PAUL]: Enter, Paul.

PAUL: Good morrow, Your Majesty.

KING: Well, sirrah?

PAUL: My brother has just left here. A clumsy lout.

KING: Ah, your brother? Same family? [JESTER *starts testing his switch.*]

PAUL: He thought he could fool you. Now I am not so vain.

KING: No?

PAUL: No. Of course I want to marry the Princess, and that is why I'm here.

KING: Yes? [QUEEN *yawns.*]

PAUL: Yes, I know I can't fool *you*. But look—only look out of the window, sire!

KING: Your brother wanted me to look in the courtyard.

PAUL: No, the window! The window!

KING: What for?

PAUL: Do you not see? There is a crow sitting in that tree, and he has three white stripes on his back. Ha! Ha! I fooled you that time!

KING: A crow with three white stripes, did you say?

PAUL: Yes, yes, three whites stripes.

KING: Well, I see a donkey in here who will soon have more stripes than three on his back. Take that, and that, and that! [JESTER *administers punishment with zest.*]

PAUL: Ow! Ow! Ow!

KING: And that!

[JESTER *gives final touch as* PAUL *runs from room.* KING *drops exhausted on his throne.* QUEEN *fans him.* JESTER *lovingly fingers switch.*]

Curtain

Scene 3

A quiet street near the palace. In one corner is a booth behind which stands the old CROCKERY VENDER *and her* DAUGHTER. *China, pots and pans, etc., in booth.*

CROCKERY VENDER: Business has been very bad today.

DAUGHTER: Yes, indeed! No one seems to want china dishes. Why don't you sell ribbons and laces?

CROCKERY VENDER: You think of nothing but vanity. Ribbons and laces, indeed! And how would you eat were it not for cups and dishes?

DAUGHTER: I would rather wear pretty things than eat any day. Then perhaps a king's son would see me and love me.

CROCKERY VENDER: King's son, indeed! [BOOTS *comes strolling along in his old, ragged clothes.*] Here comes one who is more for the likes of you!

DAUGHTER: What! That shabby fellow!

CROCKERY VENDER: Who knows? Clothes are not everything.

BOOTS [*Approaching*]: Good morrow, mother.

DAUGHTER: Mother, indeed! Not so fast, young man!

CROCKERY VENDER: Will you be quiet, foolish girl?

BOOTS: That was only in jest, young lady, I assure you.

DAUGHTER: I should hope so! Presumptuous puppy!

CROCKERY VENDER: Will you be wanting any pots or crocks, sir? I have the very finest.

BOOTS: How much will you take for the whole lot?

CROCKERY VENDER: The whole lot?

DAUGHTER: He is mad! Name a high price!

CROCKERY VENDER: Three shillings, young sir. Not a penny less.

DAUGHTER: Three shillings! Not a penny less!

BOOTS: Very well. But you must do exactly as I say.

CROCKERY VENDER: Oh yes, sir, yes sir, anything!

BOOTS: Come here and I will tell you.

DAUGHTER: Take his money first.

BOOTS: Done! Here it is, dame. [*Counting.*] One, two, three. But your daughter may not share our secret.

DAUGHTER:
       'Tis little I care.
       I'm off to the Fair,
       To buy me fine laces and bows for my hair.
Good-by, good-by! [*Exit* DAUGHTER, *dancing off stage.*]

BOOTS [*To* CROCKERY VENDER]: Will you do exactly as I say?

CROCKERY VENDER: Yes, yes! [BOOTS *whispers to old* CROCKERY VENDER.]

Curtain

Scene 4

Same as Scene 3. Old CROCKERY VENDER *with her wares at extreme end of stage as* BOOTS *enters from other end, waving away an imaginary crowd.*

BOOTS: No, I will not! I will not do it, I say! Stop pestering me! Go away! I will *not!*

KING [*Entering with* QUEEN]: Who is this, making such an uproar near my palace?

BOOTS: Sorry, Your Majesty, but I am trying to run away from all the people who are pestering me.

KING: Why should they pester you?

BOOTS: They all want to buy my cap, and I don't want to sell it.

KING: But why should anyone want to buy such a cap as that?

BOOTS: Because it is a fooling cap, the only one in all the world.

KING: A fooling cap? I should like to see you fool someone with it. [*Looking around in search of someone.*] Could you fool that old body yonder, with the pots and crocks?

BOOTS: Oh yes, that is easily done. How do you want me to fool her?

KING: Make her break all her pots and pans.

QUEEN: Your Majesty! That poor old soul!

KING: Tush, madam! 'tis but a jest! A fooling cap indeed!

BOOTS: I assure Your Majesty I have but to blow in the cap and it will obey my every command.

KING: Blow away, then!

BOOTS [*Takes off his cap very elaborately and carefully making many passes with it. Then he blows into it, solemnly*

and as he finishes, calls out]: Now break pots! Break pots!
[*Old* CROCKERY VENDER *immediately jumps up and begins breaking one pot after another.*]

KING: Upon my soul!

QUEEN: You had best buy the cap from the fellow, or he will fool the Princess away from us for sure and certain!

KING: Do you think I need you to tell me that? There is not a moment to be lost. Come, fellow, sell me the hat.

BOOTS: No indeed! Sell my precious fooling cap? No, indeed!

KING: Come, come—if I give you a purse of gold?

BOOTS: No, No!

KING: Two purses of gold?

BOOTS: No, no! My precious cap!

KING: A whole bag of gold?

BOOTS: We-e-ell, perhaps—

KING: Quick, Herald, a bag of gold! [HERALD *brings a bag of gold.* KING *throws it to* BOOTS. BOOTS *gives cap to* KING. KING *takes cap and blows in it. To* QUEEN *as he puts the cap on and places his crown on* BOOTS' *head.*] My dear, who is King now—this fellow or myself?

QUEEN: Ah, no cap can fool me, sire. It is you [*curtsying*] who are King.

KING [*Hastily taking his crown again, and dusting it off*]: I'm! It is but natural that my royalty should be so evident. Still, I am a bit disappointed. Let me think. [*Reflects.*] What ho, Page!

PAGE: Your Highness?

KING: Fetch me a lemon, Page! [PAGE *exits and returns at once with a lemon.*] Now taste it, Page.

PAGE: Must I, Your Majesty?

KING: By royal command. But wait! [*He blows long and solemnly into his cap.*] Now taste it. Is it not delicious?

PAGE [*Tastes lemon and makes wry face*]: Your Majesty, it is sour as a lemon.

KING [*Blowing into cap again*]: Take another taste, Page!

PAGE [*On his knees*]: Mercy, Your Majesty!

KING: Nonsense! You will find it so sweet it will positively cloy!

PAGE [*Tasting it again with reluctance and with still wryer face*]: No more, Your Majesty, I implore!

KING: What! Is it possible that *I* have been fooled?

BOOTS: I fear so, my liege. And now, may I marry the Princess?

KING: Not so fast, not so fast! To be sure, you fooled me, but not enough. Still, I will give you another chance, for you are a clever fellow.

BOOTS: What is my task?

QUEEN: Perhaps I can give you an idea, my lord.

KING: Let us hear it.

QUEEN: There is the Lord High Councilor, who is, next to you, the wisest man in all the world. Could you fool him?

BOOTS: It might be done.

QUEEN: Very well, then. If you can fool the Lord High Councilor so as to bring him to the castle tomorrow morning against his will, the Princess is yours.

BOOTS: I shall try, Your Majesty.

KING: Remember, he is to come against his will.

BOOTS: I shall remember, Your Royal Highness.

[*Exit* KING, QUEEN *and* HERALD. BOOTS *and old* CROCKERY VENDER *dance around joyously together.*]

    Curtain

Act III
Scene 1

    A room in the LORD HIGH COUNCILOR'S *house.* COUNCILOR *seated,* DAUGHTER *standing next to him. Enter* FIRST SERVANT.

FIRST SERVANT: Lord High Councilor!

LORD HIGH COUNCILOR: What is it?

FIRST SERVANT: Have you heard the news, Lord High Councilor?

LORD HIGH COUNCILOR: No. What is it?

FIRST SERVANT: The King has said that if Boots can bring you to the castle against your will, he may marry the Princess.

DAUGHTER: As though anyone could do that, Father! Are you not the wisest man in all the world?

LORD HIGH COUNCILOR: So I've been told.

DAUGHTER: And the cleverest?

LORD HIGH COUNCILOR: *I* think so.

DAUGHTER: Well, then! [*To* SERVANT.] Silly thing, how can he be brought to the castle against his will?

FIRST SERVANT: But, mistress, it is not *I* who say so. Such is the King's proclamation.

DAUGHTER: Foolish girl! Do not let me hear any such nonsense! No one can fool *my father!*

[*Enter* SECOND SERVANT.]

SECOND SERVANT: Master! Master!

LORD HIGH COUNCILOR: What now?

SECOND SERVANT: Master, there is something strange outside the door.

DAUGHTER: Strange? What does it look like?

SECOND SERVANT: It is a great meal sack, mistress, and somebody lying in it.

DAUGHTER: What nonsense!

SECOND SERVANT: But I assure you it is true! And all this person says as he lies in the sack is *"Sh! Sh! Sh!"*

LORD HIGH COUNCILOR: Strange—very strange! I must go and see it!

DAUGHTER: Do not go, Father! There may be danger!

LORD HIGH COUNCILOR: Very well, then, you bring the sack in here.

DAUGHTER: How wise you are, dearest Father! [*To* SERVANTS.] Go then. Don't stand gaping there!

FIRST SERVANT: But suppose he does not wish to come?

SECOND SERVANT: Yes, suppose there should be danger for *us!*

LORD HIGH COUNCILOR: Go at once, cowards that you are! [*Exit* SERVANTS, *timidly. They return, dragging the meal sack, one at each end. In the sack lies* BOOTS. *They put the sack down between the* COUNCILOR *and his* DAUGHTER.]

LORD HIGH COUNCILOR: This is indeed strange! How came you here?

BOOTS: *Sh! Sh! Sh!*

DAUGHTER: What is your business here, strange fellow?

BOOTS: *Sh! Sh!* I am not to be talked to now. This is a wisdom sack, and I am learning wisdom as fast as a drake can eat peas.

LORD HIGH COUNCILOR: What wisdom have you learned, for example?

BOOTS: Well, I have learned that the clever fellow who fooled the King yesterday is coming with seventeen tall men to take you to the castle, whether you want to, or not.

LORD HIGH COUNCILOR [*Trembling*]: And have you learned how I can get the better of this clever rogue?

BOOTS: Oh, yes, I have learned that easily enough.

LORD HIGH COUNCILOR: Oh, wise man! If you will tell me, I will give you twenty pounds.

BOOTS: No, no! Wisdom is not bought as cheaply as that!

LORD HIGH COUNCILOR: One hundred pounds, then?

BOOTS: That's better. If you will give me one hundred pounds, you may get into the sack yourself and learn all the wisdom you want, and more besides.

LORD HIGH COUNCILOR: Oh, thank you, learned man! Here are your one hundred pounds!

BOOTS: Let me help you into the sack.
[*Helps him in. Gets him comfortably settled, very ostentatiously, then suddenly pulls the string and starts off for the palace.*]

LORD HIGH COUNCILOR [*Calling and struggling*]: Help! Help! Help!

BOOTS: Call all you want, Lord Councilor! I have you safe in my bag and to the palace you go against your will. For I must and shall marry the Princess!

[*Exit* BOOTS, *dragging the* COUNCILOR, *in the sack, after him.* DAUGHTER *and* MAIDS *stand with upraised hands and open mouths, looking after them.*]

Curtain

Scene 2

KING, QUEEN *and* JESTER *in the throne room* (*same as Act I*). *Enter* BOOTS, *drawing after him the* COUNCILOR, *still kicking and struggling in the sack.*

BOOTS: Your Majesty, I have come to marry the Princess. Here is the Councilor, and I think it is plain that he is here against his will. [*More kicks from the* COUNCILOR.]

KING: Yes, I think that is reasonably plain.

BOOTS: Will you introduce me to the Princess, please?

KING: Ah, that is another matter. Royalty is not so hasty in these affairs.

QUEEN: No, indeed, our daughter is not so easily won.

KING: Why, you do not even know her! And *that* gives me an idea!

QUEEN: My clever, clever King!

KING: Thank you, my love. I deserve it, but still, thank you.

BOOTS: Do you mean there is still another task for me?

KING: Why, yes, I do! And this time it will not be so easily accomplished.

BOOTS: Speak, I beg you!

KING: If you will come tomorrow morning, you may have the Princess and welcome. *But—*

BOOTS: Yes, yes?

KING: But you must pick her out from among her maidens, who will be dressed just as she is.

QUEEN: Wonderful, Your Majesty, wonderful! The Princess is saved from this adventurer. He can never do it.

BOOTS: I shall try, Your Royal Highness. But this time you will surely give me the Princess?

KING: On my honor as a king, sir!

BOOTS: Your hand on that, Your Royal Highness.

KING: My hand, Mr. Boots! [*They shake hands.*]

    Curtain

Scene 3

    QUEEN *and* NURSE *sit surrounded by maidens, all dressed exactly alike, in white capes (covering their previous costumes, if necessary), collars of ermine and bandeaux of same.*

QUEEN: I declare, I am the Princess's mother, and it is hard for me to tell which of them all she is!

NURSE: Hush! Hush! At any moment the young man may come in. We must not give away the secret!

QUEEN: You must be most careful, Nurse. You know, as the Princess' nurse, you are the most likely to say something to her, or go over and pet her.

NURSE: I? Indeed I would do no such thing! Would I? [*Running over to* PRINCESS *and arranging her bandeau.*] Now would I, dear Princess? I wouldn't talk to you for all the world.

FIRST LADY IN WAITING: What are you doing now, silly? Quick! The young man may be peeking even now.

SECOND LADY IN WAITING: Yes, they say he is so clever he can see through a wall and hear through any door.

NURSE: You be careful, my darling, if you marry a man like that!

FIRST LADY IN WAITING: Will you stop talking to her,

Nurse! I declare, you're giving me the fidgets! Can't we do something to while away the time?

QUEEN: Why don't you dance, ladies? The new steps that the dancing master taught you last week.

SECOND LADY IN WAITING: Very well, madam. Take your places, everyone!

[*Dance. Melody suggested, Edward German's* "Morris Dances."]

NURSE: See, here comes the King. And he has with him the Lord High Councilor and a strange man. [*Turning toward the* PRINCESS.] Oh, I do hope he is a *nice* young man, my darling!

QUEEN: Will you be quiet, or must I send you from the room?

KING [*Entering with* BOOTS *and* COUNCILOR]: Here is the Princess, among the maidens. See if you can find her.

LORD HIGH COUNCILOR: Yes, see if you can find her, clever one!

[BOOTS *takes from his pocket a box. He opens it, and out of it there jumps a mouse. A mechanical toy may be used for this purpose; or, failing that, a stuffed cotton mouse, on elastic bands to make it snap from its box, will suit the purpose. There is great confusion among the girls, who scream, run, and jump on chairs. One of them faints away in the middle of the stage. When the others see this, they run to her, chafe her hands, fan her, bring her water, etc.*]

BOOTS [*Pointing to her as she rises*]: *That* is the Princess!

KING: You are right, young man. I see there is no fooling you. Take her—she is yours!

Tableau

Curtain

PRODUCTION NOTES

Costume Suggestions:
King: Straight gown; coat of fancy material, with revers, cuffs

and bottom edged with broad band of ermine; crown; jeweled chain; scepter.

Queen: Purple gown, trimmed redingote style in two rows of ermine down front, skirt ending in train also edged with ermine ("ermine" throughout descriptions is cotton batting, inked or dotted with black paper muslin); basque waist, long sleeves, lace falling over wrists; dog collar of pearls; Juliet cap—may be made of a coarse hair net with pearls sewn over it.

Jester: Red-and-yellow jester's costume, with cap and bauble.

Suitors and Herald: Very short bloomers, and stockings to match; overtunic with long sleeves, puffed and slashed at top; jeweled belt or chain; short cape; ruff; small hat with plume.

Father: Peasant's costume.

Peter and Paul: Very short bloomers, coming halfway between hip and knee, and long stockings to match. Straight, sleeveless tunics, cut in points below waist line; white shirts with turn-down collars; Peter Pan caps.

Boots: Ragged khaki trousers; long-toed cloth shoes, laced around ankles and up legs; khaki-colored jerkin, long sleeves, open at the neck. Peter Pan cap.

Crockery vender: Black or brown ragged gown; shawl over head; straggling hair; cane.

Her daughter: Peasant costume.

Lord Councilor: Long black gown—here a college gown may be used; white "George Washington" wig (can be made of cotton batting) tied with black ribbon; horn-rimmed spectacles; ferule.

Maidservants and Princess' nurse: Black or brown gowns, full skirted, kerchiefs crossed over breast; white stockings; black slippers; white Breton cap for nurse, small caps for maids.

Princess' ladies: Long white capes and round, standing collars of ermine. Ermine bandeaux.

Councilor's daughter: Dolly Varden costume of flowered cretonne, full skirt, panniers, bodice laced with narrow black velvet ribbon, black velvet ribbon at neck and wrist; wreath of small flowers; white stockings; low-heeled black strap slippers.

Princess: Who can dictate a princess's costume? Anything appropriate to the chosen period.

The Staff and the Fiddle

ADAPTED FROM HOWARD PYLE'S THE WONDER CLOCK

BY SOPHIE L. GOLDSMITH

Characters

FIDDLER

TINKER

SHOEMAKER

OLD BEGGAR WOMAN

TROLL

PRINCESS

SLAVE OF THE FIDDLE

FIRST GOSSIP

SECOND GOSSIP

MASTER SHOEMAKER

MASTER GLOVER

MASTER TAILOR

THE STAFF AND THE FIDDLE

From *Wonder Clock Plays*. Adapted from Howard Pyle's "The Wonder Clock," by Sophie L. Goldsmith. Copyright, 1925, Harper & Brothers. Copyright, 1953, Sophie L. Goldsmith.

THE STAFF AND THE FIDDLE

Act I
Scene I

A room in a little house in the woods. It is as cheerful a cottage interior as resources will permit. There is a fireplace at the side (the same one may be used throughout these plays, on the Christmas pattern), a table set for three, and bearing the eatables afterward mentioned, a bench drawn up to the table, and easy chairs, near the fireplace. In one corner is a coil of rope; in another a clothes basket. When the curtain rises there is no one on the stage. There is a knock at the door. Nobody answers. Another knock. Still no answer. Then the FIDDLER, *carrying his staff, pokes his head into the room and enters uncertainly, tiptoeing and stopping every now and then, as though afraid of trespassing. If it is possible to have the* FIDDLER *small and slender, in contrast with the* SHOE-MAKER *and the* TINKER, *it will add to various effects in the play.*

FIDDLER: Anyone at home? [*Nobody answering, he gradually makes his way into the room. He looks around, sniffs at the food on the table and then runs to the exit.*] Come along, comrades!

[*Enter, very cautiously,* TINKER *and* SHOEMAKER. *First they poke their heads in, just as the* FIDDLER *did, then gradually they enter, on tiptoe, with high and exaggerated steps.*]

129

FIDDLER [*Beckoning them impatiently*]: Come in. You need have no fear! Why, the place fits our wants like a silk stocking!

[*The two grow bolder and walk about the room, examining everything. But it is not a hasty examination, such as the* FIDDLER'S *was. They finger the tablecloth, weigh the table silver, look at the china plates to see the marks on the bottom, examine the furniture, etc.*]

TINKER: *M-m-m!* I think it will do!

SHOEMAKER: Yes, for a time, at least, we can manage.

FIDDLER: Oh, my soul! After such a walk as we have had, it looks like Paradise to me!

TINKER: Oh, I dare say it would. For some folks, the best is none too good, and others are satisfied with anything at all.

FIDDLER: Come, come, Tinker, we have traveled a weary way. Now, lost in the forest, we find food, warmth and shelter. Can we complain?

SHOEMAKER: Indeed we have traveled a weary way! Just my luck. I have walked my soles through, and I shall have to use my own leather to patch them! [*Examines shoes ruefully.*]

FIDDLER: What is the use of being a shoemaker if you cannot patch your own shoes? Cheer up, man; you shall have mine to patch as well, and likewise the Tinker's here [*giving* TINKER *a playful poke*]. Hey, Tinker?

TINKER [*Repulsing him sourly*]: Not so fast! What do you charge to mend a pair of shoes, Shoemaker?

SHOEMAKER: No more than you do for your tinkering, fellow, and a better job I make of it, I warrant you!

TINKER: What! There is not a better tinker than I, for miles around!

FIDDLER: I am sure, gentlemen, that you [*to* SHOEMAKER] are a marvel at your trade, and [*to* TINKER] that none can equal you at yours. But I am also sure that never was anyone so hungry as I. Come, what have we here? [*Goes to table and takes up a dish.*] Cheese! There is nothing like cheese, after such a journey as ours!

SHOEMAKER [*Snatching the plate from him*]: So say I! The smell of it goes to my heart! [*Starts eating cheese greedily.*]

FIDDLER [*Sarcastically*]: You are quite welcome, Shoemaker. And see here [*uncovering another dish*]—a smoking-hot sausage! Whoever lives in this house knows what is good!

TINKER [*Snatching it from him*]: I will take the sausage. I require nourishing food.

FIDDLER [*Standing, legs apart, regarding the two of them, as they eat ravenously*]: You are a pretty pair of traveling companions! I suppose I am not hungry in the least?

SHOEMAKER [*His mouth full*]: Well, eat, then!

TINKER [*Grabbing at everything on the table*]: Yes, help yourself, as I do!

FIDDLER: Somehow, the idea of doing as you do does not tempt me. I will just have a bit of the bread, which you are not touching. [*Sits down with staff at his side. Takes bread and eats it.*]

SHOEMAKER: Bread! Why should we eat bread? Here is cake, with raisins, and glowing fruit and sweets! Bread, indeed!

TINKER: Yes, we get bread at home.

FIDDLER: I am not so fortunate. Sometimes there is bread, and oftener not.

SHOEMAKER: Need you remind us of such things now? Bah, how vulgar you are!

TINKER: Yes, I suppose you would like to fiddle a tune for us on the spot, to make you think of home!

FIDDLER: That I would! I do miss my dear fiddle!

SHOEMAKER: Why did you not carry it with you, then?

FIDDLER: Oh, I expected to take only a stroll. Who would have thought I would lose my way as I did? I who know every inch of the forest!

TINKER: Strange that the same thing should have happened

to all of us.

SHOEMAKER: And stranger still that this little house seems to have no owner. [*Knock at door.*]

TINKER: In heaven's name! There he comes! [*Tries to cram down as much as possible.*]

SHOEMAKER [*Hastily replacing eatables*]: Remember, I did not start to eat! 'Twas the fiddler here! [*Another knock.*]

FIDDLER: Fools! Would the owner knock for admittance? He would walk in without knocking.

TINKER: True, true! We need not open. [*Another knock.*]

FIDDLER: Oh come—it may be another who has lost his way, as we have.

SHOEMAKER: What of it? Let him find it again.

FIDDLER: Not I. [*Calling.*] Come in, whoever you are!

TINKER: Idiot!

[*Enter the* OLD BEGGAR WOMAN. *She is bent almost double and dressed in ragged and threadbare clothing.*]

BEGGAR WOMAN: Oh, kind sirs, give a poor old woman a penny or two. Do now.

SHOEMAKER: Not I! I have barely enough for myself.

BEGGAR WOMAN [*To* TINKER]: You, sir. Have you nothing to spare me?

TINKER: Off with you, old pestilence! How dare you annoy us?

BEGGAR WOMAN [*To* FIDDLER]: And you, sir? I am hungry and tired.

FIDDLER: That I can well believe, mother. Come, sit down and rest yourself. Here is a bit of bread for you.

BEGGAR WOMAN: Thank you, thank you, kind sir. You are very good. [*Sits down and munches bread.*]

FIDDLER: Oh, as to that, mother, we are all chicks in the same puddle.

TINKER: Speak for yourself, sir.

SHOEMAKER: Indeed, yes! I am no chick and I see no puddle.

FIDDLER: No offense, old rooster, no offense!

[SHOEMAKER *and* TINKER *walk off loftily to other end of stage and seat themselves in front of the fireplace, toasting their toes and elbowing one another for the warmest place.*]

BEGGAR WOMAN: I don't want to cause any quarrel between you and your friends, sir.

FIDDLER: Oh, they are only happy when quarreling with someone. Between you and me, they are as sour as bad beer.

BEGGAR WOMAN: Well, well, the wind of heaven blows the chips and the straws together. Some day you will find better companions.

FIDDLER: Do you really think so, mother? I am pretty lonely, sometimes, I can tell you.

BEGGAR WOMAN: And what do you do when you feel lonely?

FIDDLER: Oh, I usually have my fiddle as a companion, and then nothing matters.

BEGGAR WOMAN: Good! Good! I am a pretty wise old woman, if I do say it myself, and I promise you your fiddle will bring you your greatest happiness.

FIDDLER: Thank you, mother, for your cheering words.

BEGGAR WOMAN: I must be off now. Farewell.

FIDDLER: Stay, mother. Here are two pennies to help you on your way. 'Tis not much, but such as it is, you are welcome to it.

BEGGAR WOMAN: Thank you, young sir, thank you! And now, a cake for a pie. Since you have been so kind, what would you like in the way of a wish?

FIDDLER: Nothing, thank you. I am fairly well content as I am.

BEGGAR WOMAN: But too much content is as bad as too little. I tell you I am a wise old woman. Ask what you will and your wish shall be granted.

FIDDLER: Well, then, since you are so kind, there *is* just one thing I would like.

BEGGAR WOMAN: And what is that?

FIDDLER: I am not much of a fighter.

BEGGAR WOMAN: So?

FIDDLER: No, no! You see, I am not very big. But in this world a man must fight his way. [*The line about "not very big" may be omitted.*]

BEGGAR WOMAN: True, most true. How can I help you?

FIDDLER: If it were only possible, now, for this staff here to do my fighting for me!

BEGGAR WOMAN: So be it. You have only to say "Rub-a-dub-dub," lay about you with your staff, and none can stand against you.

FIDDLER: Fine! It's rather cowardly to have to depend on a staff. But what would you? Some can fight and some can fiddle.

BEGGAR WOMAN: Now you can do both. Good luck to you! And remember, "Rub-a-dub-dub!"

FIDDLER: Rub-a-dub-dub it is! Good day, mother! And thank you!

[*Exit* OLD BEGGAR WOMAN.]

TINKER [*Turning around*]: Well, is the old hag gone?

SHOEMAKER: Or have you invited her to stay to dinner?

FIDDLER: As to that, I do not think you have left much for her.

TINKER [*Bending over to poke the fire*]: If she had stayed, she would have been cold as well as hungry. See, the fire is almost out. Who will get more wood?

SHOEMAKER: Not I. I am still footsore.

TINKER: And not I. I am too comfortable.

FIDDLER: Well, I am weary of lolling at my ease here. I shall go out into the forest and get an armful. [*Exit* FIDDLER.]

TINKER [*Settling himself still more comfortably*]: The fellow is certainly useful.

SHOEMAKER: Yes, that he is. Between you and me, we would have been in a pretty hole without him.

TINKER: But he is such a fool! [*Knock*.] Good heavens! Another beggar?

SHOEMAKER: How do I know? Open the door.

TINKER: Open it yourself! What do you take me for? [*Knock again*.]

SHOEMAKER: Well, I shall not open it. I am too busy. [*Lights his pipe*.]

TINKER: And I shall stay right here. Who knows what might happen to this chair if I left it?

[*Enter* TROLL, *ugly, humped, with a great long cudgel.*]

TROLL: Pretty manners you two have! Can you not open when a body knocks?

SHOEMAKER: And why should we open for you, I should like to know?

TROLL: Why should you not, fellow? Know you not I am a troll and have great power over all in this forest?

TINKER: Power! Pooh! We have often heard of trolls, but never met one. How are we to know you speak the truth?

TROLL: You shall have proof soon enough. Give me something to eat.

SHOEMAKER: Not a scrap. Be off with you.

TROLL: Give me some of that food at once, I tell you!

TINKER: And I tell you, you get nothing from this table.

TROLL: So that is the way the churn clacks! Well, we shall just see about that!

[*Takes his club and commences beating them with might and main. It is no use their trying to beat back, for he seems to be all over at once, and the* SHOEMAKER *and* TINKER *hop about "like two peas on a drumhead."*]

SHOEMAKER: Mercy, Troll, mercy!

TINKER: Only stop, and you shall have all the food there is!

TROLL: It is too late now, you curs. You shall suffer for treating me so.

[*Enter* FIDDLER. *He stands watching* SHOEMAKER *and* TINKER *for a moment, then fingers his staff and calls out.*]

FIDDLER: Here, here! Stop, I say!

TROLL [*Stopping and turning around*]: And who are you?

FIDDLER: Never mind who I am. Stop that beating at once!

TROLL: Hoity, toity! You shall have a taste of my club yourself, impudent fool!

[*Turns from the other two, who immediately retreat to the fireplace, groaning and rubbing themselves. They get behind the chair and watch from over the back. The* FIDDLER *grasps his staff firmly. The* TROLL *lifts his cudgel high.*]

FIDDLER [*Just before the* TROLL'S *cudgel descends, in a loud voice*]: Rub-a-dub-dub!

[*He starts beating the* TROLL *so that he now hops and dances around the stage just as the others did. Standing up on their chairs, the* TINKER *and* SHOEMAKER *laugh at the* TROLL *and applaud the* FIDDLER. *After this has gone on for a short time, the* TROLL *runs out of the room.*]

FIDDLER [*Running after him, calling out to the others*]: My, what fun it is to fight with such a staff! I'll finish him off now and then come back to you. [*Exit* FIDDLER, *brandishing his staff.*]

SHOEMAKER [*Coming out from behind the chair*]: "Finish him off," indeed! Cannot he leave well enough alone?

TINKER: Said I not he was a fool? We were just getting the better of the Troll, when he comes and steals our victory.

SHOEMAKER: Well, for my part, he is welcome to his victory. Oh, how sore I am!

TINKER: And I! I ache in every joint. What a devilish little Troll he is. [*They rub themselves pityingly.*]

[*Enter* FIDDLER, *rushing in, out of breath.*]

FIDDLER: Quick! Quick! I saw where he went!

SHOEMAKER: Well and good. If only he will stay there, we are happy.

FIDDLER: Come! There is not a minute to lose. I chased him until he reached a great hole in the ground. And in there he popped, like a frog into a well.

TINKER: In heaven's name, let him stay there, then!

FIDDLER: Never! Who knows what prisoner he may be keeping there? Let us after him quickly!

SHOEMAKER: Not I! I am a mass of bruises.

TINKER: Not I! I could not walk a step.

FIDDLER [*Raising his staff as if to strike again*]: Would you like to see more of my fighting, gentlemen?

TINKER: What! You would not dare!

FIDDLER: Would I not? [*Approaches* TINKER *slowly and threateningly, swinging his staff.*]

SHOEMAKER: I—I think we shall reconsider, Fiddler. But do not ask us to go down into the hole, I beg of you!

FIDDLER: Have no fear of that. I am saving the cream of the adventure for myself.

TINKER: You are welcome to such cream, Fiddler. Do you not agree, Shoemaker?

SHOEMAKER: Oh, entirely, entirely. But how can you get down into the hole?

FIDDLER: I have thought of that. You two shall lower me into it. Bring me yonder basket, Tinker. [*Pointing to corner of stage.*]

TINKER [*Limps over to corner as directed, with very bad grace. He drags from it a clothes basket, groaning at every step as he does so*]: Here it is.

FIDDLER: And there [*pointing to other corner*] is some rope, if I mistake not. Do you [*pointing to* SHOEMAKER] bring it hither.

SHOEMAKER [*Glances at* TINKER, *who looks at* FIDDLER *and taps his forehead significantly.* SHOEMAKER *shrugs his shoulders and, also limping at every step, brings the rope to* FIDDLER]: You are right, Fiddler. And good, stout rope it is.

FIDDLER: Good! When we get to the hole, you two shall lower me into it, as I direct, and then we shall see what we shall see.

TINKER [*Significantly*]: We shall see!

SHOEMAKER [*Emphatically*]: We shall!

FIDDLER: Very well, then—forward, march!

[*Exit* TINKER *first, dragging basket.* SHOEMAKER *trailing the rope,* FIDDLER *following with outstretched staff, which he now and then flourishes, and at which they cringe in terror.*]

> *Curtain*

Act II
Scene I

The home of the TROLL. *The impression should be as dark and gloomy a one as possible. This may be accomplished by the use of black hangings, table covers, etc., wherever possible, and dark table and chairs, whereas in the little house in the woods the furniture was light and the cretonne gay. In the back of the stage is a chest or closet, from which the eatables are taken and from which the* SLAVE OF THE FIDDLE *later emerges. In a corner, awaiting the right moment, hangs the* FIDDLE, *but it cannot be seen by audience. In the center is a table* (*with black cover*) *and two chairs. On the ground at side are a couple of heavy stones. The* PRINCESS *and the* TROLL *are seated together.*

PRINCESS: Ah, me! how long it is since you have brought me to this dreadful place!

TROLL: Dreadful place, indeed! Is it not snug and warm?

PRINCESS: It is so dark that no ray of sunlight ever comes here. Who can be happy without sunlight?

TROLL: Nonsense! Think of all the good things that grow in darkness. Mushrooms now—there's a delicacy for you!

PRINCESS: Mushrooms! You forget I am a princess! We give mushrooms to the pigs.

TROLL: And there's myself and my family. Do we burn extravagant candles, I ask you, or require a great, silly sun before we can go about our business?

PRINCESS: Ugh! You horrible creature! Will no one ever come to my rescue? [*Starts to weep.*]

TROLL: Weep as much as you like, Princess. You know we trolls prefer tears to laughter—though your very tears are not gloomy enough. You are such a joyful creature.

PRINCESS: I was joyful once, before you carried me off and imprisoned me here. But now I have forgotten how to smile.

TROLL: Oh, smiling would be out of place here. Besides, you have such a dazzling smile—it lights up this whole place and makes things very hard on me! [*Voice,* FIDDLER'S, *from without.*]

FIDDLER: Hallo there! Anyone at home?

PRINCESS [*Clasps her hands and smiles*]: Oh, at last, at last! Come—come quickly!

TROLL: You little fool! Stop smiling! The whole place is illuminated!

FIDDLER: Hello—hello! Is it much further down?

PRINCESS: Oh, come—come quickly!

TROLL: Be quiet, you! How dare you call out!

PRINCESS: I will! I will! I will if I die for it! [*Putting her hands to her mouth.*] What ho, there! What ho-o-o! Come quickly!

TROLL [*Rushing forward with club upraised and shaking her threateningly by wrists*]: You will, will you?

PRINCESS [*Calling*]: Whoever you are, come, and come quickly!

[*She and the* TROLL *struggle together for a moment, until* FIDDLER *appears at side of stage, standing upright in his basket, which has been pushed onto the stage.*]

FIDDLER [*Calling to* TINKER *and* SHOEMAKER, *off stage*]: All's well! Let go now, boys. When I have need of you, I will call. [*Stepping out of basket and striding over to where* PRINCESS *and* TROLL *are struggling. The* TROLL *is so amazed that he drops his club and stares at the* FIDDLER, *open-mouthed.*] Oho! So this is your lair! Then it is rub-a-dub-dub again. But this time I shall make short work of you, you toad! [PRINCESS *covers her face with her hands.* FIDDLER *strikes the* TROLL *very coolly and scientifically three times. At the first stroke the* TROLL'S *knees tremble under him. At the second he drops upon them and holds out his hands for mercy. And at the third he falls over dead. At the thud the* PRINCESS *looks up.*]

PRINCESS: Oh, sir, how can I ever thank you?

FIDDLER: Madam, do not mention it, I beg. 'Tis but a small service to render a princess.

PRINCESS: How do you know I am a princess?

FIDDLER: Oh, 'tis easy to tell true royalty.

PRINCESS: And are you, then, a prince?

FIDDLER: Alas! no, madam, though I thank you for a pretty compliment. I am but a poor fiddler.

PRINCESS: No matter, no matter. None has ever done me such a service before. That wicked Troll yonder [*pointing to* TROLL *and shivering*]. Oh, take him away! Take him away!

FIDDLER: Here, you miserable wretch! [*Bundles* TROLL *into basket and calls up to* SHOEMAKER *and* TINKER.] Hallo, there! Hallo!

SHOEMAKER AND TINKER: Hallo, hallo!

FIDDLER: Pull up the basket and dump out what you find there, quickly, and send it back again! [*Basket is withdrawn.*] And now, lady, comfort yourself. He will never trouble you again.

PRINCESS: Oh, how happy I am! For over a year he has kept me in this dreadful place, and I was beginning to despair of ever leaving it.

FIDDLER: But that is all over now, Princess. Do not think more about it.

PRINCESS: How tired you must be, after all your exertions! May I offer you any refreshment?

FIDDLER: Well, now that you mention it, I *am* a bit thirsty. Could you give me a drink?

PRINCESS: Alas, that a princess should not be able to offer any drink to her brave deliverer! Unless perhaps you are partial to ink?

FIDDLER: *Ink?*

PRINCESS: Or shoe polish?

FIDDLER: But Princess!

PRINCESS: You see, the Troll could not abide anything that was not black, and so he satisfied his thirst with ink and shoe polish.

FIDDLER: My poor, poor Princess!

PRINCESS [*Going to chest and bringing out articles as she talks*]: But in the ice chest there is a large supply of licorice and blackberry pie. Would you like some of that?

FIDDLER: If you will share it with me.

PRINCESS: Gladly, gladly! And here are black radishes and black bread, too. It is not very cheering fare, but my father, the King, will soon atone for that. [*As she finishes setting articles on table.*] I drink my deliverer's health in blackberry pie.

FIDDLER: And I swear you eternal fealty on a stick of licorice!

[*They raise pie and licorice aloft and eat. Voice from without—the* SHOEMAKER'S.]

SHOEMAKER: Hallo there, Fiddler! We have buried the Troll. What next?

PRINCESS: Who speaks?

FIDDLER: Friends of mine. They are waiting to rescue us.

PRINCESS: Oh, let us go, quickly!

FIDDLER: Very well, Your Highness. [*Going to side of stage and raising hands to mouth.*] Tinker and Shoemaker, draw the basket up with care. You will bear a precious burden!

SHOEMAKER: Another troll?

FIDDLER: No, a princess—a lovely princess. [PRINCESS *curtsies.*]

TINKER: Ah-h-h!

FIDDLER: Have a care now, you rascals! If aught go wrong with her, you shall have a taste of my staff!

SHOEMAKER: We will be most careful, Fiddler.

PRINCESS: Oh, I am afraid of the journey!

FIDDLER: You need have no fear, Princess. Just seat yourself in the basket, and my friends will draw you up to safety.

PRINCESS: Then let us go quickly!

FIDDLER: Here is the basket, Princess. See, it is quite cozy! [*Helps her into the basket and arranges her skirts about her.*]

PRINCESS: But are you not coming with me?

FIDDLER: Go you first, and I will follow. The basket will be too heavy otherwise.

PRINCESS: [*Starting to weep*]: Oh, I cannot go alone!

FIDDLER: Indeed you can! Think of the sunshine and the palace and the King, your father, awaiting you!

PRINCESS [*Sniffing a bit*]: True, true. I need all my royal [*sniff*] courage. Farewell, Fiddler. But as it may be some time before we are alone together, take this love token from me. [*Draws ring from her finger and gives it to* FIDDLER.]

FIDDLER: Your Highness!

PRINCESS: Indeed, yes! We are sweethearts now, and I shall never wed another. Perhaps court etiquette will forbid my telling you so at the palace. After all, this place has its merits!

FIDDLER: Lady, I cannot tell my joy. Remember, I am but a poor fiddler!

PRINCESS: But I am a discriminating princess.

FIDDLER: After all, what is a fiddle between sweethearts?

PRINCESS: Fiddlesticks!

FIDDLER: Exactly! [*Embraces her.*]

PRINCESS: Farewell for a few moments!

FIDDLER: Farewell! [*Calling to* SHOEMAKER *and* TINKER.] The Princess is ready to start. Careful now, or it shall cost you dear!

SHOEMAKER: All shall go well, Fiddler! Have no fear!

FIDDLER: Farewell again, Princess. Courage!

[PRINCESS *is pulled out, waving farewell and blowing kisses to* FIDDLER. FIDDLER *responds ardently.*]

Curtain

Scene II

The same as Scene I. The FIDDLER *is alone, waiting for the basket to come back. As the curtain rises he is pacing up and down the stage, stopping every now and then as he talks.*

FIDDLER: Heavens! If only the Princess doesn't fall out of the basket as easily as she fell in love! Oh, what a sweet Princess she is, and what a lucky Fiddler I am, and what slow fellows the Tinker and Shoemaker are! Will that basket never come! [*The basket is pushed onto the stage.*] At last—hurrah! I am off! [*Is about to step into the basket when a thought strikes him.*] Wait a bit. There are tricks in every trade. Suppose the Shoemaker and the Tinker are planning one for me! Better put a substitute passenger into that basket and see how it fares. [*Looks about, finds a large stone and puts it in the basket.*]

SHOEMAKER [*From outside*]: Are you safely seated?

FIDDLER: All ready! Pull away!

[*Basket, with stone in it, is drawn off stage.* FIDDLER, *legs apart, hands in pockets, head upraised as though watching its ascent, awaits developments. In a moment, the basket, the rope holding it cut, is thrown violently on the stage, so that the stone comes tumbling out. Voices of* PRINCESS, SHOE-MAKER *and* TINKER *from behind side scenes.*]

SHOEMAKER: That's the way to treat upstart fiddlers! Good riddance to you!

PRINCESS: Oh, my poor Fiddler, what is become of you now?

TINKER: Never mind him. You come along with us.

PRINCESS: Farewell forever, Fiddler! They are forcing me away!

FIDDLER: Be of good courage, lady! Many a one has been in a bad hole and gotten out again.

SHOEMAKER: Ha! Ha! Ha! Boast all you like. It won't be easy to get out of *that* hole, I warrant you!

FIDDLER [*Shaking his fist*]: We shall see!

TINKER: We shall see! Farewell, braggart!

FIDDLER: Perhaps they are right. This is a deeper hole than I have ever been in. [*Picking up staff and talking to it.*] Of what good are you to me now, old Rub-a-dub-dub? I can no more get out of this pickle than a toad out of a cellar window. [*Sits down dejectedly with his head in his hands. After a moment, he jumps up.*] Come now! I may as well die cheerfully, if need be. Let us have a look about here. Perhaps there may be another prisoner hidden somewhere. Who knows? [*Starts walking about. Looks under table, under chairs, into chest, etc. Suddenly, in the corner, he spies the violin. He seizes it.*] Aha, there is some butter to the crust, after all! Have you been here all this time, old friend, and I never knew it? Come along, let us have a bit of a jig to cheer us up!

[*If the person taking the* FIDDLER'S *part is a real musician, he may play an entire piece before the* SLAVE OF THE FIDDLE *makes his appearance. Anything lively may be used, such as the "Perpetuum Mobile" or a Strauss Waltz or Moskowsky's "Spanish Dance," etc. If the actor is not able to play the instrument, he may merely make a pretense, and someone behind the scenes can play a few bars of any lively dance tune, to which the* FIDDLER *dances as he plays. He has been playing for some time, according to his ability and the enjoyment of the audience, when, suddenly, three loud taps are heard. He stops playing.*]

FIDDLER: Strange! What can that be? [*Listens intently. Loud raps are repeated.*] There's no mistake this time. Can it be that there really is another prisoner here? [*Calling.*] Where are you? [SLAVE OF THE FIDDLE *answers from the chest or closet at back of room.*]

SLAVE: Do you wish to see me, master?

FIDDLER: Of a surety I do!

SLAVE: Here I am!

[*The chest or closet at back of stage opens, and the* SLAVE OF
THE FIDDLE *appears. He should be as small as possible in comparison with the* FIDDLER, *but if that is not feasible, he should
make up in grotesqueness of costume what he lacks in contrast of size—perhaps an Oriental effect, to give the impression of the magic and bizarre. The* SLAVE *steps out of the
chest and approaches the* FIDDLER, *before whom he kneels.*]

FIDDLER: Welcome, stranger!

SLAVE: What would you have, master?

FIDDLER: Information, first. Who may you be?

SLAVE: I am the Slave of the Fiddle, master. You have but
to play, and I appear, ready to grant whatever you may wish.

FIDDLER: So. Is that the tune we play? Many a one would
give his all for such a fiddle!

SLAVE: But not everyone could play on it, master. I come
only to those who have the courage to make music, instead
of bewailing their fate.

FIDDLER: Look here, are you a preacher or a slave?

SLAVE [*Kneeling and touching floor with head*]: Whatever
master wishes, I shall perform.

FIDDLER: Very well, then. Put me to sleep until the middle
of next week, and then take me wherever the Princess is.

SLAVE: But why wait until the middle of next week?

FIDDLER: I wish to test the love of the Princess. If it can
endure until the middle of next week, it is deep indeed.

SLAVE: Ah, what courage you have! It is a privilege to
serve such a master!

FIDDLER: Say you so, indeed! Put me to sleep, then, and
mind you guard well my staff and my fiddle!

SLAVE: So be it, master. Sleep!

[*He makes a few passes with his hands. The* FIDDLER *cradles his head on his fiddle and, shaking the staff warningly at the* SLAVE, *falls asleep.*]

Curtain

Act III
Scene I

A bit of road. Two GOSSIPS *are standing, knitting as they talk.*

FIRST GOSSIP: Whoever heard the like? To think that that sourfaced Tinker will wed our Princess!

SECOND GOSSIP: Not so! The Shoemaker swears he will have her.

[*Enter* FIDDLER. *He stands listening to them.*]

FIRST GOSSIP: I tell you 'twas the Tinker who rescued her from the Troll!

SECOND GOSSIP: And I with my own eyes saw the Troll's head, which the Shoemaker keeps nailed outside his window.

FIDDLER [*Coming forward*]: Who is this brave Shoemaker of whom you speak?

FIRST GOSSIP: You must come from afar not to know who he is.

FIDDLER: I am a stranger. Pity my ignorance.

FIRST GOSSIP: You know, of course, that a year ago our beautiful Princess was carried off by a troll?

FIDDLER: Yes, I have heard of that.

SECOND GOSSIP: He carried her to his home, deep down in the ground, and there he kept her his prisoner for a year and a day.

FIDDLER: Lucky Troll!

FIRST GOSSIP: The Shoemaker declares that he labored night and day, making his way down into that dreadful hole—

SECOND GOSSIP: And the Tinker vows that, had it not been for his aid, she would never have been found.

FIRST GOSSIP: And they both claim the glory of the Troll's death, and the hand of the Princess, as the King promised.

FIDDLER: What is that about the King's promise?

SECOND GOSSIP: Do you not even know *that!* The King vowed that whoever rescued her is to have her for his wife, and half of the kingdom to boot.

FIDDLER: Of course, if he put it in those words, the Shoemaker should have her.

FIRST GOSSIP: And why?

FIDDLER: There is half of the kingdom *to boot!*

FIRST GOSSIP: Out upon you, fiddling punster!

[*Enter* PRINCESS, SHOEMAKER, TINKER *and* KING. PRINCESS *walks with the* KING, *disdainfully keeping the other two at a distance.* FIDDLER *hides behind* GOSSIP *so that he is not seen.*]

KING: Now, my dear, do be reasonable. Would you have me break my royal word?

PRINCESS: Would you have me break my royal heart? I tell you I shall wed neither of these fellows.

KING: And why? Think of a tinker or a shoemaker always on hand. What a load off a housekeeper's mind!

PRINCESS: Ah, I had far rather listen to music whenever I had a mind to!

KING: Forget your sentimental dreams, my dear. Music is all very well in its place, but you see it did no good in the Troll's den.

PRINCESS: But I have told you again and again that I owe my freedom to the Fiddler, and not to these boors.

KING: Where is the fellow, then? Why does he not come and claim you?

TINKER: If your story were true, and he had been powerful enough to kill the Troll and send you to safety, could he not save himself as well?

SHOEMAKER: Perhaps he has found another princess more to his liking, in another troll's den?

PRINCESS: Oh, you wretches! You know well how to torture

a helpless Princess!

KING: It *is* possible that the young man may have changed his mind. I believe you yourself have done so once or twice?

PRINCESS: You, my own father, to insinuate that a man could turn from me to *anyone!*

KING: It has happened with brave men and lovely princesses, before, my dear.

PRINCESS: I shall not listen to you. And yet [*Aside*] 'twas I who first declared love. What if they should be right!
[*Starts to weep.*]

SHOEMAKER: Come, Princess, dry your eyes and choose between us. If we cannot fiddle for you, we have our good points also.

PRINCESS: Oh, I hate you both! I hate you!

KING: At least give them their chance, my dear. If you still insist that they did not kill the Troll, assign them another task and see how they perform it.

TINKER: Good! Only name the task!

PRINCESS: Very well, then. I vow and declare I shall marry no one—no one—who cannot bring me a pair of pure golden slippers, with a real diamond buckle on each slipper.

TINKER: But, Princess, such slippers would be most cumbersome!

PRINCESS: Did I ask your advice, fellow? I have spoken. It is for you to act.

SHOEMAKER: I have made slippers all my life, Princess. But golden slippers! And diamond buckles! I have neither the tools nor the material.

PRINCESS: What is that to me? I shall marry nobody until I have such slippers [*Exit* PRINCESS *haughtily.*]

KING: I did my best for you, gentlemen. But comfort yourselves—even her Fiddler could not grant such a wish.
[*Exit* KING, *shaking head.*]

FIRST GOSSIP [*Steps forward. As she does so,* FIDDLER *hides behind* SECOND GOSSIP. *When* SECOND GOSSIP *talks, he hides behind* FIRST GOSSIP *again, etc.*]: If you ask me, I think she favors you, Shoemaker. Else why should she want slippers?

SECOND GOSSIP: True enough! Courage! I know the Master Shoemaker of the town, and between the two of you, you should be able to make the slippers.

SHOEMAKER: Oh, fetch him quickly! Go! [*Exit* SECOND GOSSIP.]

TINKER: Well, I may as well give up hope at once, as far as I am concerned. Besides, the Princess does not suit me. I know other maids far more to my taste.

FIRST GOSSIP: Oh, how sour the grapes are, Tinker!

SHOEMAKER: I am not sure of that, Gossip. Even if I could make the slippers, think what a clattering there would be about the house!

FIRST GOSSIP: Faint heart! You do not deserve the Princess! [*Enter* SECOND GOSSIP, *with* MASTER SHOEMAKER. MASTER SHOEMAKER *is old and walks with a cane.*] But, see, here comes the Master Shoemaker himself. Ask him.

MASTER SHOEMAKER: What is this I hear about golden slippers and diamond buckles?

SHOEMAKER: It is the Princess's demand, Master Shoemaker. She will not wed until she has such a pair.

MASTER SHOEMAKER [*To* SHOEMAKER]: Can you make them?

SHOEMAKER: Alas, no!

MASTER SHOEMAKER: Indeed! I thought the young people could do everything much better than their fathers these days!

SHOEMAKER: Do not taunt me, Master Shoemaker! I want the Princess above all things. Can you help me win her?

MASTER SHOEMAKER: Not I, young shoemaker! You must try elsewhere.

TINKER: Come, all is not lost yet. Let us go to her again. One of us may bring her to her senses.

SHOEMAKER: I would I could use the slipper *on* her, the obstinate hussy!

[*Exeunt* TINKER *and* SHOEMAKER, *shaking fists defiantly.*]

FIRST GOSSIP: There go a fine couple of wooers! The one is so craven he tries not at all, and the other is almost as bad.

SECOND GOSSIP: Let us follow them and see what they are after. We have naught to do but to mind other folks' business!

FIRST GOSSIP: True, true! How easy that is! Let us hurry, lest we miss something! [*Exeunt* GOSSIPS, *gossiping as they go.*]

FIDDLER [*Stepping forward*]: Master Shoemaker!

MASTER SHOEMAKER: Yes.

FIDDLER: Will you take a journeyman shoemaker?

MASTER SHOEMAKER: What can you do?

FIDDLER: I can make a pair of slippers such as the Princess wants.

MASTER SHOEMAKER: What!

FIDDLER: I swear I can.

MASTER SHOEMAKER: Who are you?

FIDDLER: No matter. I can make the slippers, and you shall yourself bring them to the Princess.

MASTER SHOEMAKER: H'm! I am a trifle old for such junketings. However, I am interested professionally. Let me see what you can do.

FIDDLER: Very well, then. Leave me alone for a few moments. When I want you, I shall call.

MASTER SHOEMAKER: Indeed! It is not often a journeyman shoemaker gives orders to his master.

FIDDLER: Have it your own way. I shall go to the other shoemaker and offer my services to him.

MASTER SHOEMAKER: No, no! It shall be as you wish. You promise to call me the moment you have finished?

FIDDLER: The very moment. But, mind you, leave me entirely alone and see that no one interrupts me!

MASTER SHOEMAKER: On my word of honor!

[*Exit* MASTER SHOEMAKER, *hobbling away as fast as he can.* FIDDLER *starts to play his violin. Enter* SLAVE OF THE FIDDLE.]

SLAVE: What would you have, master?

FIDDLER: I wish a pair of slippers such as the Princess has

ordered, but I want only one buckle to the pair.

SLAVE: Why do you not ask me to render you a real service, master? Your tasks are too simple.

FIDDLER: Come, come, prove it to me. Up to now you have not failed me.

SLAVE: Nor shall I do so now, master. Here [*drawing slippers from his pocket*] are the slippers. Have you any other commands?

FIDDLER: Not just now, Slave. You may go. [*Exit* SLAVE *with salaam.*]

FIDDLER [*Calling*]: Master Shoemaker! Ho, there, Master Shoemaker.

MASTER SHOEMAKER [*Running in*]: Here I am, Journeyman.

FIDDLER: And here are the slippers. [*Hands them to him.*]

MASTER SHOEMAKER [*Examining them*]: Upon my word! There is something in the younger generation, after all. Young man, I congratulate you!

FIDDLER: Oh, it is nothing—nothing! A mere knack.

MASTER SHOEMAKER: Knack, indeed! It is the work of an artist! But—

FIDDLER: Yes?

MASTER SHOEMAKER: Do you know that there is only one buckle to the pair?

FIDDLER: Oh, as to that, do not trouble yourself. Just take the Princess aside and tell her that the Fiddler has the other, and matters will be as smooth as cream.

MASTER SHOEMAKER: Very well, Your Worship. Good day, Your Worship. I am off to the palace at once, Your Worship.

[*Exit, bowing himself out obsequiously, slippers hugged to his breast.*]

FIDDLER: My Worship has done a good day's work, it seems to me! And now to see what my Princess has to say! Come, My Worship, let us go to the palace together! [*Struts off stage, fiddle under arm, staff in hand.*]

    Curtain

Scene II

A room in the palace. KING, PRINCESS, SHOEMAKER *and* TINKER. PRINCESS *is looking away from all three and tapping her foot impatiently.*]

PRINCESS: It is fully an hour since I asked for the slippers, and not a sign of them.

SHOEMAKER: Dear Princess—

PRINCESS: I am *not* your dear Princess.

SHOEMAKER: Not as yet, Your Royal Highness. But if you will only allow me to prove to you how much more useful a leather slipper is than a golden one—

[*Enter* MASTER SHOEMAKER, *bearing before him upon a cushion the golden slippers and stepping out majestically. He is followed by the two* GOSSIPS *and the* FIDDLER, *who hides behind now one and now the other, as he did before.*]

TINKER: Look! Look! As I live, here are the slippers!

MASTER SHOEMAKER [*Kneeling before* PRINCESS]: Your Highness, I have the honor to present to you the slippers, just as you ordered them.

PRINCESS: Impossible! Let me see them! [*Examines them excitedly.*] What beauteous things! Can it be possible that *you* have made them?

KING: Which do you prefer, Daughter—the old man with his golden gift or one of these young bloods here?

PRINCESS: Wait! Wait! [*To* MASTER SHOEMAKER] Are these slippers your own work, sir?

MASTER SHOEMAKER: I—I supervised their manufacture, lady.

PRINCESS: I ask you, are they your own handiwork?

MASTER SHOEMAKER: Oh, handiwork is only a part of artistry, madam. It is the soul which endures, and my soul [*kneeling*] was in that work, lady.

PRINCESS: H'm! Your soul appears to have its limitations, sirrah. There is one buckle missing.

SHOEMAKER: Aha!

TINKER: Oho!

MASTER SHOEMAKER: A trifle—a mere trifle. A word in your ear, madam.

PRINCESS: Be brief, fellow.

MASTER SHOEMAKER [*Whispering*]: The Fiddler has the other buckle, madam.

PRINCESS: What! The Fiddler, say you?

MASTER SHOEMAKER: That is what the fellow calls himself —a young journeyman stripling who helped me with this job.

PRINCESS: Oh, praise heaven! Praise heaven! [*Hugs the* MASTER SHOEMAKER.]

MASTER SHOEMAKER: Oh, madam, I little thought such honor would be mine!

PRINCESS: *Yours?* Don't be foolish! *Yours?* Where is that journeyman shoemaker? Take me to him at once.

MASTER SHOEMAKER: How impetuous you are, lady! I know not where he is, upon my word. He disappeared as soon as this little task was completed.

PRINCESS: Little task, indeed. Never were there such slippers, never, never!

KING: Do your raptures mean that you will wed the fellow, Daughter?

PRINCESS: Oh, I am not yet ready to wed anyone, sire.

KING: *What?*

PRINCESS: No, these slippers have but whetted my appetite for tributes. Now I would have—

TINKER: Yes, yes!

PRINCESS: Such slippers are useless unless—

MASTER SHOEMAKER: Speak on, lady, we implore!

PRINCESS: Unless I have a pair of gloves to match them.

KING: You have dozens of gloves.

PRINCESS: Not fine enough. They must be of the finest silk, all embroidered with silver and pearls, and with a ruby clasp at the wrist of each.

KING: I am beginning to feel sorry for your husband.

SHOEMAKER: There is not a glover in the town that can make such.

FIRST GOSSIP [*Stepping forward and curtseying at every step*]: If you please, Your Highness, my cousin owns a glove shop. Mayhap he could make the gloves?

TINKER: These women are too well acquainted hereabouts! Mind your own business, Gossip!

PRINCESS: Fetch your cousin, the glover, by all means, my good woman. [*Exit* FIRST GOSSIP. FIDDLER *keeps hidden behind* SECOND GOSSIP.] As for me, I shall put these slippers away with the care due them.

KING: I, too, shall go. Your absurd orders make me look too ridiculous, Daughter.

PRINCESS: Nonsense! A king is never ridiculous unless he is too easily satisfied. Come, then, if you are so minded.

[*Exeunt* KING *and* PRINCESS, PRINCESS *lovingly carrying her slippers.*]

MASTER SHOEMAKER: Well, I cannot see what my zeal has gained for me. Not even a word of thanks! By heaven! I shall stick close to leather after this. [*Starts to go.*]

SHOEMAKER: One moment, Master Shoemaker. Just tell me how you made those slippers—do, now!

MASTER SHOEMAKER: Not I! The secret dies with me! But see—here comes the Master Glover!

[*Enter* MASTER GLOVER *with* SECOND GOSSIP.]

MASTER GLOVER: Good day, all. What is this I hear? For I do not trust our good Gossip here.

TINKER: This time she is right, the old chatterbox! Her Highness the Princess demands a pair of gloves of the finest silk—

SHOEMAKER: All embroidered with silver and pearls—

MASTER SHOEMAKER: And with a ruby clasp at the wrist of each.

ALL: Ha! Ha! Ha!

FIRST GOSSIP: Set to work, Master Glover. Get busy at once.

MASTER GLOVER [*Turning to* SECOND GOSSIP *in a passion*]: Had I known you brought me here to make sport of me, wretched woman, I should have stayed at home. Be off with you!

[*Exeunt both* GOSSIPS, *running*. FIDDLER *gets behind* MASTER GLOVER.]

MASTER GLOVER [*Turning to others*]: And as for you, Master Shoemaker, a little success has turned your old head! Away, before I forget the respect due your gray hairs!

MASTER SHOEMAKER: Nay, my triumph did me no good, Master Glover. See that yours has more lasting effects.

[MASTER GLOVER *starts after him threateningly*. MASTER SHOE-MAKER *dodges him and hobbles off stage*.]

TINKER [*To* SHOEMAKER]: I see no use in our remaining here. Let us annoy the Princess a bit.

SHOEMAKER: A good thought! Come along! [*Exeunt* SHOE-MAKER *and* TINKER, *arm in arm*.]

FIDDLER [*Stepping forward*]: Master Glover!

MASTER GLOVER: How now! Another mocker!

FIDDLER: Oh, no, sir, far from it! I am only an humble apprentice.

MASTER GLOVER: An apprentice, hey? Well, what can you do?

FIDDLER: For one thing, I can make a pair of gloves such as the Princess demands.

MASTER GLOVER [*Raising his cane*]: Did I not say I would endure no more mockery? Be off with you, you saucy varlet!

FIDDLER: Oh, but I am not mocking you, Master Glover. It is you who can mock the others, if you will hire me.

MASTER GLOVER: Humph! Talk, talk! You will have to show me what you can do.

FIDDLER: Give me a room to myself, and I will show you

just such a pair of gloves as the Princess asks for.

MASTER GLOVER: That is a queer request.

FIDDLER [*Shrugging shoulders*]: I cannot work otherwise.

MASTER GLOVER: It can do no harm to try you out. But, mind, if this be some jest, it shall go hard with you!

FIDDLER: On my word, Master Glover, it is no jest.

[*Exeunt* MASTER GLOVER *and* FIDDLER, MASTER GLOVER *shaking his finger threateningly at* FIDDLER, FIDDLER *protesting.*]

    Curtain

    Scene III

    A room in the GLOVER'S *house. It is furnished with only a table and chair. Enter* MASTER GLOVER *and* FIDDLER.

MASTER GLOVER: Step this way, young fellow. 'Tis not much of a room, but you will be undisturbed here.

FIDDLER: You promise to let no one near me?

MASTER GLOVER: I promise. Be as quick as possible, fellow!

FIDDLER: Oh, I shall work rapidly, never fear!

MASTER GLOVER: Farewell then. I leave you alone.

[FIDDLER *plays upon his fiddle. Enter* SLAVE OF THE FIDDLE.]

SLAVE: Good morrow, master. How did the Princess like the slippers?

FIDDLER: She is not yet satisfied. She must have more.

SLAVE: What! Is she a centipede, then?

FIDDLER: Not more slippers, Slave! But more proof of your ability.

SLAVE: Aha! You touch me in a tender place there. Whatever you wish shall be granted.

FIDDLER: Could you give me a pair of gloves for her now, of the finest silk, all embroidered with silver and pearls, and with one ruby clasp?

SLAVE: Master, you are making game of me. This is mere child's play.

FIDDLER: Come, then, play away. If it be so easy, you should work quickly.

SLAVE: It is so simple, it is done before you ask me. Here [*drawing gloves from his pocket*] are the gloves.

FIDDLER: True enough, just as she ordered them! Indeed, you are a jewel of a Slave!

SLAVE: It is my joy to serve you, master.

FIDDLER: Good! Rejoice, then, for I have other work for you. Pay close attention!

SLAVE: Master, you have only to command.

FIDDLER: After the Glover takes these gloves to the Princess, you and I shall start for the palace together. But you are to make us both invisible to those around us.

SLAVE: There is nothing easier, master.

FIDDLER: Can I fiddle when I am invisible?

SLAVE: Indeed, yes.

FIDDLER: Is it painful to be invisible?

SLAVE: Only to your vanity, master.

FIDDLER: Very well, then. Make yourself invisible now, and I shall call the Master Glover. [SLAVE *bows and walks to back of stage.*] Ha! You are gone already. I feel very strange without you!

SLAVE: You can have me back to the tune of a fiddle, master.

FIDDLER: Just a bit longer. What ho, Master Glover!

MASTER GLOVER [*Running in*]: Well, young whippersnapper, have you cooled your heels by now?

FIDDLER: Cooled my heels, indeed! In a moment, I shall be off to the Princess with these, myself!

MASTER GLOVER [*Observing gloves for first time*]: What! Did you really succeed in making them, then? Let me see them! Let me see them!

FIDDLER: Here they are, Master Glover. Are you satisfied?

MASTER GLOVER: Satisfied? You are a genius, boy, a genius! But why is there only one clasp?

FIDDLER: Do not trouble yourself about that, Master Glover.

If the Princess takes any note of it, lead her aside secretly and tell her that the Fiddler has the other, and she will be satisfied.

MASTER GLOVER: Very well, very well! Oh, me, what a triumph! Wait until I catch the Master Shoemaker—I'll put a flea in his ear, I warrant! [*Rushes out, carefully carrying gloves.*]

FIDDLER: And never a thought of me! When I have married the Princess, I shall not forget those who have helped *me,* I hope! Are you there, Slave?

SLAVE: Yes, yes, master!

FIDDLER: Make me invisible and bring me to the palace—quickly, now! [*Beckons imperiously to* SLAVE, *who bows and comes forward.*]

　　　Curtain

　　Scene IV

　　A room in the palace. Enter FIDDLER *and* SLAVE.

FIDDLER: I have the strangest feeling! Although you say I am invisible, I can see everything and everybody.

SLAVE: You shall have proof in a moment, master. When the King and Princess enter, you may pass in front of them, even touch them, and they will not know of your presence.

FIDDLER: I am anxious to try it.

[*Enter* KING *and* PRINCESS *and seat themselves on thrones.* FIDDLER *makes a low bow before the* PRINCESS. *She looks straight at him, but does not see him.*]

PRINCESS: I thought to have my gloves by now, but there is not a soul here.

KING [*Also looking straight at* FIDDLER *and* FIDDLER'S SLAVE]: Yes, the room is empty.

FIDDLER: I grow bolder. [*Pokes the* KING *in the side.*] Thank you for the compliment, Your Majesty!

SLAVE: Did I not tell you that you could be neither seen

nor heard?

FIDDLER: What a good child I am, to be sure! But see, here come the gloves.

[*Enter* MASTER GLOVER, *bearing gloves before him on a golden tray—a piece of cardboard covered with gold paper. Behind him come the two* GOSSIPS, *the* MASTER SHOEMAKER, *the* MASTER TAILOR, SHOEMAKER *and* TINKER. *The* FIDDLER *and* SLAVE *retire to one side. During this scene the* FIDDLER *can do a good deal of byplay, mimicking, making remarks, sotto voce, etc.*]

MASTER GLOVER: Princess, since your wish became known, I have worked night and day, and I think I have succeeded in making you the gloves you requested.

PRINCESS: Indeed! You are bold, knave!

MASTER GLOVER: Do but look upon the gloves, lady, and see if they please you.

PRINCESS: They are indeed beautiful! [*Trying them on.*] And how well they fit! How did you know my size?

MASTER GLOVER [*Sighing sentimentally*]: Ah, love is a great teacher, Princess!

FIDDLER: Impudent liar!

SLAVE: Calm yourself, master.

PRINCESS: But see here—

MASTER GLOVER: I know what you are about to say. There is one clasp missing.

PRINCESS: Exactly.

MASTER GLOVER: Truth to tell, I had a little help in that part of the work from an apprentice.

FIDDLER: How noble of you to admit it!

PRINCESS: Ah! Go on, go on!

MASTER GLOVER: When I reproached him for his carelessness, he shrugged his shoulders and said [*leaning forward and whispering to* PRINCESS], "Just tell her the Fiddler has the other clasp."

KING [*Leaning forward eagerly*]: *What* did he say?

MASTER SHOEMAKER [*Also leaning forward*]: I did not understand that part, either.

SHOEMAKER, TINKER, AND OTHERS [*All craning necks*]: We, too, would like to hear.

PRINCESS: Would you, indeed? Oh, with what impertinent curiosity I am surrounded! Well, you shall not hear. [*To* MASTER GLOVER, *taking him aside.*] Tell me again.

MASTER GLOVER: He said, "Just tell her that the Fiddler has the other clasp."

PRINCESS: Oh, how happy I am! How happy I am!

KING: Shall I order the wedding cake, Daughter?

PRINCESS: If you like, but first—

FIDDLER: Pay close attention, Slave!

SLAVE: Master, I am all ears.

KING [*Sinking back in his chair*]: I feared it! I knew it! You will never be satisfied!

PRINCESS: No, Your Majesty, I shall not marry until I have a wedding dress of white silk, with both sleeves looped up with pearls as big as marbles.

[FIRST *and* SECOND GOSSIPS, *one on each side of him, pull forward the* MASTER TAILOR, *who seems reluctant to come and hangs back.*]

FIRST GOSSIP: Silly fellow! Here is your chance!

SECOND GOSSIP: The Master Shoemaker and the Master Glover have succeeded. Why should you fail?

MASTER TAILOR: But what would it avail me to try? The Princess would never marry me, anyway.

PRINCESS: Come forward, fellow. Your modesty is quite refreshing.

MASTER TAILOR: I have not the skill, madam. Indeed I have not!

[PRINCESS *argues with* MASTER TAILOR *in pantomime, while the others shrug their shoulders, frown, or tap their feet with impatience, yawn, laugh, etc., while* FIDDLER *and* SLAVE *have ensuing dialogue.*]

FIDDLER: Now is our time, Slave. I command you to throw all this company into a deep sleep.

SLAVE: Very well, master. You have but to play a tune on your fiddle, and they shall sleep until you order them to awake.

[FIDDLER *plays "Rockabye Baby" or Brahms' "Guten Abend" or Schumann's "Slumber Song" or Grieg's "Lullaby," etc., etc. As he plays,* SLAVE *goes about making mysterious motions, until the whole company is asleep in various characteristic attitudes.*]

FIDDLER: To work! The Princess' wedding dress. Quickly, now! But loop up only the one sleeve with pearls.

SLAVE: Will you not vary your method, master?

FIDDLER: Do you wish me to lock you up in the Troll's den again? Do as I say!

SLAVE [*Bows. Goes to back of stage and picks up the dress, which has been concealed behind a bit of drapery, a chair, or what-not*]: Here is the gown, master.

FIDDLER [*Examining dress*]: I am a man, but I cannot but admire so beautiful a garment. Indeed, you are a priceless slave!

SLAVE: That is nothing, master, nothing. Why not let me give you a real proof of my skill? I can turn you into a dragon if you say the word.

FIDDLER: No, I thank you, not today.

SLAVE: Or, at your lightest bidding, I can transport you to the loveliest gardens of the Orient, where beautiful princesses shall be your willing slaves.

FIDDLER: One Princess is enough, I thank you. And there [*waving an arm*] she lies.

SLAVE: Ah, you have no spirit for adventure!

FIDDLER: Wait until I am married to the Princess. She will keep us so busy gratifying her wishes that we shall have no time for adventures!

SLAVE: Have you any other commands?

FIDDLER: Yes. [*Carries dress over to* MASTER TAILOR *and lays it in his lap.*] Awaken them now, but keep us both still invisible.

SLAVE: Your fiddle, master, your fiddle! Without it I can do nothing.

FIDDLER: Nor I. Heaven bless it!

[*Starts to play "Hark! Hark the Lark!" or "Phoebes Arise" or a reveille.* SLAVE OF THE FIDDLE *goes around touching all, until they gradually awake.*]

MASTER TAILOR [*Finding dress on his lap*]: Do I dream? Or have I really made the gown the Princess ordered? Princess!

PRINCESS [*Yawning and rubbing her eyes*]: Yes.

MASTER TAILOR: Princess, your gown is here, just as you ordered it!

PRINCESS: Tailor, Tailor, show it to me! [*Examines the dress eagerly.*] Yes, and it is all complete, excepting that only one sleeve is looped up with the pearls I ordered. Why?

MASTER TAILOR: Lady, I know nothing of it. It seemed to me that I fell fast asleep, and when I awoke the gown was here as you see it.

TINKER: Fool! He spoils our chances!

PRINCESS: After all, you are an honest fellow. I like that.

FIDDLER [*To* SLAVE]: This won't do! I'll not have her liking any fellows excepting myself.

SLAVE: Hurrah! Now for a bit of action!

FIDDLER: Come, you have made her her bridal dress. Now clothe me as befits a bridegroom.

SLAVE: Come with me, master. None shall be finer than you.

[*Exit* SLAVE OF THE FIDDLE *and* FIDDLER.]

PRINCESS [*Rising*]: Give heed, all of you! I swore that this should be my bridal dress, and now I go to array myself as a bride. Make ready the feast, for today I choose my bridegroom!

KING: At last!

ALL: At last!

[*Exit* PRINCESS, *gown over arm. There is a great bustle as she goes out. A long table is pulled forward, chairs placed, flowers strewn, etc. In the midst of the preparation—*

Curtain]

Scene V

The stage is set, ready for the PRINCESS' *wedding party. There is a long table and everyone is at his place. The entire cast is assembled, excepting the* FIDDLER *and his* SLAVE.

KING: Good folks all, the great moment is at hand. The Princess is about to make up her mind.

ALL: Hurrah!

PRINCESS: Are we all here?

ALL: Yes, yes!

PRINCESS: Then drink to the health of my bridegroom!

SHOEMAKER: But who is he?

PRINCESS: That you will know in good time.

MASTER SHOEMAKER: Only tell me, do I remind you of him ever so little?

PRINCESS: He has your skill, but he has not used it for so many years.

MASTER TAILOR: You liked my honesty—you said so.

PRINCESS: Gentlemen, you have all helped me make my decision. But—

SHOEMAKER: Come, let us all kneel before her. When she sees us at her feet, she cannot resist at least one of us.

TINKER: Yes. The suspense is awful.

[*All suitors arise from the table and kneel before the* PRINCESS, *one behind the other, all holding one hand on heart, the other outstretched to her. Enter the* FIDDLER, *very gayly dressed— a transformation easily effected by means of a cape, a hat with plumes, and jeweled orders and chains. In one hand he holds his fiddle, in the other his staff.*]

FIDDLER: I beg your pardon. I hope I am not interrupting?

KING: On this great occasion, all are welcome, sir.

PRINCESS: This is my wedding feast, sir.

FIDDLER: Indeed! And are you marrying all these gentlemen?

PRINCESS: No, I have not yet made my choice.

ALL SUITORS [*Groaning*]: Not yet!

FIDDLER: Will you drink a glass of wine with me, lady? It may help you.

PRINCESS: With all my heart. A glass of wine for our guest! [*One of the* GOSSIPS *runs forward with a glass of wine, which she presents to him. He takes it and drops into it the ring which the* PRINCESS *gave him in the* TROLL'S *den.*]

FIDDLER [*Tasting wine*]: To your speedy and happy decision, Princess! [*He passes the glass to her. She drinks from it.*]

PRINCESS: Strange! Something seems knocking against my lips! [*She finishes drinking the wine.*] A ring! [*She takes it out of the glass and holds it up.*] My own ring, that I gave the Fiddler in the Troll's den!

SUITORS: The Fiddler! All is lost!

[*From their knees they drop to stupid sitting postures on the floor, resting back on their hands, legs outstretched, heads shaking, various expressions of chagrin and anger on their faces.*]

PRINCESS: My mind is made up at last. There [*pointing to* FIDDLER] is my sweetheart, and I will wed no other.

SUITORS [*All arising together*]: We shall see about that!

FIDDLER: We shall. Rub-a-dub-dub! [*Raises his staff threateningly.*]

PRINCESS: Not on our wedding day, dear one. Make them dance to a different tune.

FIDDLER: Is that your latest wish, Princess?

PRINCESS: My very latest.

FIDDLER: Very well, then. So be it.

[*Draws fiddle from under his cloak and starts playing. This is a good opportunity to bring in the class, camp, or favorite air. The* SLAVE OF THE FIDDLE *appears.*]

SLAVE: Any orders, master?

FIDDLER: Yes. A clergyman, at once!

[*Carefully clasping his fiddle in one hand and his staff in the other, he embraces the* PRINCESS.]

    Curtain

PRODUCTION NOTES

Fiddler: Long, tight-fitting hose, almost like tights; patches; shoes covered with same material as tights, wrinkled loosely below ankle and carried out to long points at tips, stuffed there with cotton to retain shape; figured or flowered shirt, with short sleeves, Eton jacket; Peter Pan cap with long quill.

Shoemaker and Tinker: Practically same as Fiddler, except that they have differently shaped coats, instead of his more Bohemian Eton, and caps of different shape—old-style English bonnets or draped hats.

Old woman: Black or brown ragged gown; shawl over head; straggling hair; cane.

Troll: One-piece, tight-fitting green suit, long sleeves, shoes like Fiddler's; hump on back, face made hideous and large as possible in comparison with body—flapping ears, mop of hair, etc.

Princess: Who can dictate a princess' costume? Anything appropriate to the chosen period.

Slave: Oriental costume, or Nubian slave.

Gossips: Peasants' costumes.

Master Glover, Master Tailor and Master Shoemaker: Same type of costume as those of Tinker and Shoemaker, somewhat more elaborate and having short capes with their master's emblems of glove, shoe and scissors displayed on them.

The Merry Christmas Elf

BY AILEEN FISHER

Characters

WRITER
SCHOOL CHILDREN
THREE GIRLS
CHRISTMAS ELF
MRS. FUDDY
TWO BIG BOYS
SMALL BOY
BROTHER
SISTER
NEWSBOY

Setting: Outdoors on Pine Street in Middleton

THE MERRY CHRISTMAS ELF

AT RISE: *The stage is empty for a moment. Then the* WRITER *comes in slowly. He looks at the snow on his coat sleeve.*

WRITER: Why, it's beginning to snow. Maybe that will be something to write about today, for my column in the *Middleton News*. For my daily bit of wisdom and wonder. Snow! [*Laughingly looks up at the sky and calls out.*] Who's fluffing up the pillows of the sky and sending down a shower of little white feathers? Who's dusting the ashes off the stars? Who's shaking down white petals from the wild plum trees along the Milky Way? [*Looks at sleeve again.*] Who's cutting all these fancy shapes from tissue-paper ice? [*Listens.*] I guess they're all too busy up there to answer me. [*To audience.*] Yes, my friends, it's beginning to snow in Middleton. In a little while, the sidewalk here along Pine Street will be white. When school is out [*Consults watch.*] in a few minutes, the children will be thinking of getting out their sleds. Any time they see ten feathers of snow coming down, they think of sleds. Maybe *that* will be something to write about . . . [*There is the sound of Christmas music offstage, getting louder, then fading out.* WRITER *listens intently.*] That must be Eddie Clark's sound truck. Eddie owns the radio store on the corner of Main Street and Fourth. He owns the only sound truck in town. He always gets it out at this time of year and plays the proper music. Maybe that's something to write about . . .

Every note like a gaily-dressed dancer, whirling right out into the winter air, dancing up Pine Street and down Spruce, dancing through the white petals falling from heaven, dancing into your heart. Christmas music is like that, don't you think? It waltzes around even after Eddie Clark's sound truck turns the corner. [*Consults watch.*] Well, today is the last day of school before Christmas vacation. They're probably all having parties and Christmas trees over at the schoolhouse. I remember how it used to be: A head full of jingle bells! A heart full of tinsel and meadowlarks! A hand full of [*Looks at snowy sleeve.*] . . . of diamond dust! [*There is a racket offstage.*] Hold on . . . here they come, the first bunch of them. . . . [WRITER *backs out of the way as a group of excited* CHILDREN *cross the stage.*]

BOYS *and* GIRLS: It's snowing! What did you get? I'll trade you . . . Let's go sliding on Randall's Hill. . . . Susie says she believes in Santa Claus . . . Look at it snow! Christmas vacation . . . white Christmas! [*The* CHILDREN *exit, all except* THREE GIRLS *who have come in at the end of the group. They have their arms around each other and are gaily singing "Deck the Halls." Every time they sing the "fa la la" refrain, they do a little jig in unison. At the end of the second verse, they see the* WRITER *and stop.*]

GIRLS: Oh! We didn't know we had an audience.

WRITER: That song makes me think of . . . of a flock of bright birds perched all over a fir tree, singing of sunrise, singing of spring, in the midst of a winter world. Isn't there any more? Please!

GIRLS: There's another verse. [*They sing the third verse. At the end of the song, they laugh and run out.*]

WRITER [*Trying to do the little jig*]: Fa la la la la, la la la la. It gets under your skin, doesn't it? It makes you feel good, doesn't it? [*He jigs again, then stops suddenly and looks around.*] Well, I'm certainly glad there wasn't anyone around to see me doing a thing like that . . . right in the middle of the sidewalk . . . in the middle of Middleton. Why did I do it? Maybe *that's* something to write about. What is there about Christmas coming?

CHRISTMAS ELF [*Dancing in gaily*]: There's me. [*Whirls around and stops near the* WRITER.] Maybe that isn't good English, but you know what I mean.

WRITER [*Staring at* ELF]: No, I don't. Who are you?

ELF: I'm someone to write about! [*Teasingly.*] Weren't you looking for something to write about?

WRITER: Have you been listening in on me, you rascal?

ELF: I've been watching you all the time, ever since you asked who was throwing down the snow. In fact, that's what drew me to you. [*Laughing.*] Why didn't you think of the shepherd?

WRITER: What shepherd?

ELF: The one who makes the fleecy clouds. Maybe he lost some wool. [*Mimics tone of voice of* WRITER *and looks up at sky.*] Who's throwing down some wool out of the fleecy clouds?

WRITER [*Laughing*]: I guess I did forget about the shepherd. [*Looks* ELF *over.*] Come on, who are you?

ELF: That's what you have to find out, Mr. Writer. But I'll give you a hint:

> I'm not of this world, I'm sad to say,
> Excepting once a year.
> When Christmas is through I'm shut away,
> With all my magic cheer.
> Just once in a year, for a little while,
> Folks think of the Christ Child's birth,
> And open their hearts, and sing and smile,
> And welcome me here on earth.
> But I'm not telling you who I am!
> You have to guess.

WRITER: You wouldn't be one of those dancers who seemed to hop out of Eddie Clark's sound truck, on a bar of music? You wouldn't be one of those bright red birds that seemed to

flock around when the girls sang? You wouldn't be music
. . . come to life? Wouldn't *that* be something to write about!

ELF: Guess again. Guess again. You're warm, but I can't
say you're hot. [*Skips around, then stops and looks down the
street.*] Who's that coming?

WRITER: It looks like Mrs. Fuddy.

ELF: She doesn't look very happy.

WRITER: Oh no, not Mrs. Fuddy. She carries too much of
the world around on her shoulders. But just wait till she sees
you, all dressed up in red and green. That ought to cheer her
up.

ELF: But she won't see me.

WRITER: You mean you're running away? You're going to
hide?

ELF: I'm staying right here. But she won't see me. Nobody
sees me! I'm invisible.

WRITER: But . . . *I* see you.

ELF: Oh, you're different. You believe in . . . [*Looks up
at sky.*] . . . in petals from the wild plum trees along the
Milky Way. You're not afraid to think about magic things.
[MRS. FUDDY *comes in, looking tired and cross.*]

WRITER: Good afternoon, Mrs. Fuddy.

MRS. FUDDY: What's that? Just a moment, please. [*She
opens her purse, takes out a pencil and pad, and makes a
note.*] I just thought of something else I have to get for the
church decorations. [*Replaces notebook and pencil and looks
up.*] What did you say?

WRITER: I said, "Good afternoon, Mrs. Fuddy."

MRS. FUDDY: Well, I don't know how good it is. Snowing
and all. Look at it! Makes the walks so messy. I ought to
have my galoshes on right now, but I simply haven't time to
go home for them. So much to do! You're that writer who
does a daily column for the *Middleton News,* aren't you? Why
don't you write a piece about the busy, bothersome days before Christmas?

WRITER: Bothersome?

MRS. FUDDY: Yes, yes. All those things to do. Shopping, and baking, and worrying about costumes for the Christmas pageant, and writing cards, and making wreaths, and serving on the Christmas-basket committee, and . . .

WRITER: Bothersome? [ELF, *who has been listening, suddenly dances over to* MRS. FUDDY *and blows a kiss at her cheek.*]

MRS. FUDDY [*With a start, putting up her hand*]: A snowflake . . . right on my cheek. Imagine. Only it seemed warm . . . not cold at all. [*She begins to smile.*] Well, I guess bothersome *isn't* the right word. [ELF *touches her other cheek.*] Another snowflake! And so warm. [*She is really smiling now.*] No, I'm *sure* it isn't the right word. Definitely not bothersome. We want to do all those things . . . to make Christmas bright and happy. It's really amazing, isn't it? All the things we can do. Oh, there's something wonderful about the holiday season.

WRITER [*Looking mischievously at the* ELF]: You know, Mrs. Fuddy, a sprightly little elf, all dressed in red and green, just ran up and planted a Christmas kiss on each of your cheeks.

MRS. FUDDY: Oh, you writers! You're always making up stories . . . out of snowflakes. [*Laughing and happy, she exits.*]

WRITER: Well! What did you do to her? Who are you?

ELF [*Dancing around*]:

> I'm not of this world for very long.
> But if they'd let me stay,
> I'd turn each frown to a merry song
> And chase all cares away.
> But I'm not telling you who I am.

WRITER [*Thoughtfully*]: You're not like the rest of us, are you? The snow doesn't stay on your coat or cap at all.

ELF: That's because I'm invisible! [*There is a noise off-*

stage, as if more CHILDREN *were coming from school.*]

WRITER: Careful. Here come some more children from school. [*Moves out of the way.*]

ELF:

> They will not hear me make a sound,
> Or see me here at all,
> But they *feel* me all around—
> The big ones and the small.

[*Two* BIG BOYS *hurry in with a* SMALL BOY *tagging at their heels.*]

1st BIG BOY: Look, it's snowing! Let's go coasting tonight.

SMALL BOY [*Eagerly*]: Can I go, too?

1st BIG BOY: Naw, you're too small. You stay home and go to bed, like a good little boy!

2nd BIG BOY: You'd be a nuisance.

SMALL BOY: No, I wouldn't. Honest. I never went coasting at night. [ELF *skips over and taps the two* BIG BOYS *with his pointed cap.*]

1st BIG BOY [*Suddenly pleasant*]: Never went coasting at night? You better come along then. You don't know what you've missed.

2nd BIG BOY [*Cheerfully*]: Sure. Come along. We'll show you the ropes. [*The* BOYS *exit.* BROTHER *and* SISTER *come in quarreling.*]

SISTER: It's not fair. You got six pieces of candy and I got only five.

BROTHER: Don't blame me. I didn't fill those Christmas stockings. Teacher did.

SISTER: It isn't fair. You've got to give me half the extra one.

BROTHER: I don't either.

SISTER: You do, too. [ELF *slips over and taps* SISTER *and* BROTHER *with cap.*]

BROTHER [*Suddenly merry*]: Look, Sis. I'm going to give that extra piece to Mom.

SISTER: To Mom! [*Pleased.*] Why, yes. And I'm going to give one of mine to Buddy.

BROTHER: I'll save one for Pop. Say, why didn't we think of it before? [*They exit happily. A noisy group of* CHILDREN *come in talking and shouting.* ELF *stands up like a musical director, using his cap for a baton, and starts to sing "Joy to the World." One by one, the* CHILDREN *join in until all are singing. Toward the end of the song, they exit singing merrily.*]

WRITER: I've got it! [*Takes a pad and pencil from his pocket and begins to write.*] I've got the angle! [ELF *tries to look over* WRITER'S *shoulder, but he is too small. He runs to the wings and brings in a box, climbs up on it and is able to see what* WRITER *is writing.*]

ELF [*Reading over* WRITER'S *shoulder*]: "A strange thing happened this afternoon as I was walking along Pine Street, wondering what to write about. There was something in the air—something besides the soft white flakes floating down from heaven, something besides the jolly music tumbling out of Eddie Clark's sound truck. Something warming and wonderful . . ." [WRITER *moves on, writing as he goes.* ELF *has to get down from box and keep moving it along in order to read over* WRITER'S *shoulder.*] "Did you ever feel as if your heart were full of April robins? As if a hundred candles were suddenly lit in your head? That's the way I felt this afternoon, my friends, when the strange thing happened. It was just as school was letting out. A group of children passed . . . and then, suddenly . . . I saw the Spirit of Christmas . . . in person! [ELF *excitedly jumps down from the box and runs to face* WRITER, *tugging at his coat.*] How did you *know?* How did you *know?*

WRITER [*Laughing*]: I guessed from the very beginning, but I didn't want to let on. I guessed from the moment you said you were only allowed to come on earth once in a while. How did you say it exactly? I'd like it for my column.

ELF [*Slowly, as* WRITER *writes*]:

I'm not of this world, I'm sad to say,
Excepting once a year.
When Christmas is through I'm shut away,
With all my magic cheer.
Just once in a year, for a little while,
Folks think of the Christ Child's birth,
And open their hearts, and sing and smile,
And welcome me here on earth.

WRITER [*Excitedly*]: Wait till my story about you comes out in the paper. Maybe things will be different then. What a story! I'll rush it right around the corner to the *News* office . . . so they can get out a special edition!

[WRITER *exits, writing as he walks.* ELF *skips around him and exits, too, leaving the box behind. For a moment the stage is empty. Then* MRS. FUDDY'S *voice is heard at the other side of the stage.*]

MRS. FUDDY [*Offstage*]: Lovely. Just lovely! [MRS. FUDDY *comes in, carrying Christmas greens. She is followed by* CHILDREN *with greens and small Christmas trees, wreaths, red bells, etc.*] We can start decorating the church right away. I never *saw* such lovely greens. And such heavy ones! [*She rests a minute, shifting her load in her arms.*] Where did you get them?

A BOY: Mr. Gentry showed us a place on his farm. He said the trees needed to be trimmed anyway.

A GIRL: He told us we could have all we wanted. My arms are breaking! [*She loses a bough and stoops to pick it up, but loses another. Every time she retrieves one bough, she drops another. Other* CHILDREN *laugh. Then they too begin to lose part of their load.* ELF *comes dancing in. Since he is supposed to be invisible, the* CHILDREN *must act as if they do not see him at all. Everyone seems to be having a jolly time, in spite of their troubles with the slippery greens.*]

MRS. FUDDY: So fragrant! I don't know *when* Christmas has been such fun. [*She sees the box the* ELF *left.*] Why, look, there's a box. Right in the street. I wonder how it got there.

GIRL: Let's put some of our decorations in it, so we won't keep dropping them. [*As* MRS. FUDDY *and* CHILDREN *put things in the box, the* SMALL BOY *comes in with his sled.* ELF *skips over and touches him on the shoulder.*]

SMALL BOY [*Calling out*]: Want me to help? Want me to haul the box on my sled? I could do it . . . easy.

MRS. FUDDY: That would be fine. Do you think there is enough snow?

SMALL BOY: Sure. [*They lift the box on the sled.* SMALL BOY *beams.*] You know what? I'm going coasting tonight on Randall's Hill . . . with the big boys!

MRS. FUDDY: You are? That's splendid. [*They start out with sled and greens.*] *Oh, isn't Christmas wonderful?* [*The* THREE GIRLS *who sang "Deck the Halls" come in.*]

1st GIRL: Maybe we could think of some new steps. [ELF *hurries over and taps each of them lightly on the head with his cap.*]

2nd GIRL: I've thought of something better. Why don't we practice some carols . . . and then go out and sing them to the old folks at the County Farm . . . on Christmas Eve?

3rd GIRL: Why don't we? I bet they don't have much of a Christmas out there.

1st GIRL: We could sing "Hark! The Herald Angels Sing."

2nd GIRL: And "The First Noel."

3rd GIRL: And "Silent Night." Let's.

[*A* NEWSBOY *comes hurrying in with papers.*]

NEWSBOY: Extra! Extra! Read all about it. Strange Happenings on Pine Street This Afternoon. Extra! Extra! [ELF, *excited and pleased, dances around* NEWSBOY *trying to get a look at the paper.*]

GIRLS: On Pine Street? [*They look around them.*]

MRS. FUDDY [*Hurrying in*]: Did I hear you say Pine Street, boy? Wait a minute . . . [*She gets a coin from her purse and buys a paper; starts to look at it eagerly.*]

SMALL BOY [*Running in with sled*]: What happened?

NEWSBOY: Extra! Extra!

TWO BIG BOYS [*Hurrying in*]: What's it all about? [BROTHER *and* SISTER, *and several of the* CHILDREN *who carried greens, gather around.*]

A GIRL: Read it out loud!

A BOY: Read it, Mrs. Fuddy.

MRS. FUDDY [*Turning to* CHILDREN]: What do you think? The man who writes the daily column in the *News* says that he saw the Spirit of Christmas . . . in *person* . . . on Pine Street this afternoon. He says he actually saw the Spirit of Christmas. [*The* ELF *is having a wonderful time, listening and watching.* NEWSBOY *exits, shouting "Extra! Extra!"*]

A BOY: How can you see a spirit?

MRS. FUDDY: That's just it. That's what is so strange.

A GIRL: Maybe he made it up.

MRS. FUDDY: No . . . it doesn't sound like it. [*Suddenly.*] You know, something *did* happen on Pine Street this afternoon. I don't mean to say that I saw the Spirit of Christmas, but I felt something. I definitely *felt* something. [*Puts hand to cheek.*] I was coming along, all tired and cross and hurried, and then, suddenly, something like a warm snowflake touched my cheek. And everything was different! [*She looks around her.*] It happened just about here, I believe. I wasn't tired or cross any more.

1st BIG BOY: Yeah, that's right. I felt something too, somehow.

2nd BIG BOY: All of a sudden I thought it would be nice to take my little brother along sliding.

SISTER [*To* BROTHER]: It was just about here you thought of giving Mom the extra piece.

THREE GIRLS: And suddenly we got the idea of going out to the County Farm to sing, on Christmas Eve. We were standing right here.

A BOY: What else does it say?

MRS. FUDDY [*Reading from paper*]: "This afternoon I stood on Pine Street while the jeweler in the sky was sifting down diamond dust from heaven. I was wondering what to write about. And then, all of a sudden, with my own eyes, I saw the Christmas Elf—skipping and dancing around me. I saw the Spirit of Christmas, come to earth. And there, before me, as I watched, I saw the Elf turn frowns into smiles . . . like turning thistles into roses. I saw him change selfishness to kindness . . . like turning on the light of the sun in a dark corner. I saw him turning cawing crows into canaries. I saw him change ill-will into good fellowship . . . like changing Scrooge into Santa Claus! [ELF *slips out to find the* WRITER.] With a kiss on the cheek, or a tap on the shoulder, or just a wave of his red arm, he changed everything in a twinkling. Why, oh why, do we shut away the magic of Christmas as soon as Christmas is over? Why do we close our hearts to the Spirit of Christmas as soon as the holidays end? Why don't we keep him with us—always?"

CHILDREN [*To each other*]: Why? Why?

MRS. FUDDY: Why? [ELF, *pulling* WRITER, *comes in.* WRITER *stands far at side, listening.* ELF *dances around, then taps the* THREE GIRLS *gently. They step forward and begin to sing to the tune of "Jolly Old St. Nicholas."*]

THREE GIRLS:

> Christmas comes but once a year,
> Christmas cannot stay,
> But its fellowship and cheer
> Need not go away.
> Let's all try to keep the elf
> Of Christmas in our hearts
> When the Old Year's on the shelf
> And the New Year starts!

[ELF *dances out in front of the group, waves arms like a music director, and all sing "Deck the Halls" or some other appropriate Christmas carol.*]

PRODUCTION NOTES

Characters: 6 male; 5 female; Elf may be male or female. Male and female extras.

Playing time: 20 minutes.

Costumes: All of the characters should wear everyday winter clothing except the Elf, who is dressed in red and green and has a pointed cap with a bell on the tip.

Properties: Purse, pencil and pad for Mrs. Fuddy, pad and pencil for the writer, box for Elf, greens, wreaths, bells, sled for small boy, newspapers, Christmas stockings for brother and sister.

Setting: Outdoors on Pine Street. No furnishings are necessary but if furnishings are desired, a street sign, some bushes, a fence, etc. may be placed on the stage.

Lighting: No special effects.

Mr. Popper's Penguins

ADAPTED FROM THE BOOK BY FLORENCE AND
RICHARD ATWATER

BY LULA WRIGHT

AND HER FOURTH GRADE AT LINCOLN SCHOOL,

TEACHERS COLLEGE, COLUMBIA UNIVERSITY

Characters

NARRATOR

MR. POPPER

JANIE

EXPRESSMAN

CAPTAIN COOK

BILL

POLICEMAN

DOCTOR

PERFORMING PENGUINS

MRS. POPPER

SERVICEMAN

MR. GREENBAUM

ADMIRAL DRAKE

GRETA

TWO LADIES

TWO CHILDREN

MR. KLEIN

MR. POPPER'S PENGUINS

Mr. Popper's Penguins is a modern, humorous and completely absurd story involving an untidy house painter, his wife, two children, and a pet penguin. The penguin arrived at the Popper home via "AIR EXPRESS," all the way from the South Pole. The story is filled with lively adventures, surprises and absurdities. These funny happenings placed in a modern family environment almost convince the reader that it might be possible to bring up a family of penguins in the refrigerator, train them and travel around the country exhibiting them.

One of the Fourth Graders liked the story so much she had "read it five times." She reported that "it is full of funniness and would make a perfect play." She told the story to the group and sold the idea of making it into a play. One point in favor of choosing this book to make into a play was the fact that the whole class could be in it. One child's comment was, "We can use them all for performing penguins."

Great values are derived from making a favorite story into a play. There is the satisfaction of working together on a common enterprise and sharing the fun, humor and pleasure with one's peers. This was very evident during the production of this play, for there is a joy-giving quality in the story. Its nonsense brings laughter and eases tension.

Mr. Popper's Penguins makes a delightful play.

A Street in Stillwater

MR. POPPER, *with buckets and ladder, passes down the street.* CHILDREN *coming home from school wave and call to him.*

CHILDREN: Hello, Mr. Popper. How is Janie? Can she come out to play?

MR. POPPER: Hello, children. Janie's fine. I guess she'll be out soon.

MRS. SMITH: That's Mr. Popper, the house painter.

MRS. JONES: All the children seem very fond of him.

MRS. SMITH: Oh, they love him. He tells them stories of the North Pole or the South Pole—or whatever it is. I guess he'd rather be a scientist than a housepainter.

MRS. JONES: He looks like a very nice man.

MRS. SMITH: Oh, he is—but he's kind of dreamy-like. Last year he painted our kitchen and made three sides of it green and the other side of it yellow. Dreaming about explorers, I guess. Well, I guess I must be getting on with my shopping. Good-by.

Act I
Scene I: *Kitchen at 432 Proudfoot Avenue*

MR. POPPER: Well, my love, the decorating season is over. I've painted all the kitchens and papered all the rooms in Stillwater. There's no more work until spring, when the people will want their houses painted.

MRS. POPPER: Sometimes I wish you had the kind of work that lasted all year, instead of just from spring to fall. Oh, it will be very nice to have you at home for vacation, but it will be a little hard to sweep with a man sitting around reading all day.

MR. POPPER: I could decorate the house for you.

MRS. POPPER: No, indeed! Last year you painted the bathroom four different times—and that's enough of that! But I'm worried about money. I've saved a little and I guess we can get along as we have other winters, but no more roast beef, no more ice cream, not even on Sundays.

JANIE: Are we going to have beans every day?

MRS. POPPER: I'm afraid so. Anyway, go wash your hands for supper. And Papa—put away this litter of paints, because you won't be needing them for quite a while.

Later That Evening

MRS. POPPER: What are you reading?

MR. POPPER: A book called *Antarctic Adventures*. It tells all about the different people who have gone to the South Pole, and what they found there.

MRS. POPPER: Don't you ever get tired of reading about the South Pole?

MR. POPPER: No, I don't. Of course, I'd much rather go there than read about it.

MRS. POPPER: Well, I think it must be very boring down there. It sounds very dull and cold, with all that snow and ice.

MR. POPPER: Oh, no. You should have gone with me to see the movies of the Drake Expedition at the Bijou last year.

MRS. POPPER: Well, I didn't—and I don't think any of us will have money for movies now.

MR. POPPER: If you'd gone, my love, you'd see how beautiful the Antarctic is. But I think the nicest part of all are the penguins. They're the funniest birds in the world. They don't fly like other birds, they walk erect like little men. It would be very nice to have one for a pet.

MRS. POPPER: Pets! First it's Bill wanting a dog, then Janie begging for a kitten. Now you want penguins! But I won't have any pets around! They make too much dirt in the house. Anyway, we have the bowl of goldfish.

MR. POPPER: Penguins are very intelligent. Listen to this, Mama. It says here that, when they want to catch some shrimps, they all crowd over to the edge of an icebank. Only they don't just jump in, because a sea leopard might be waiting to eat the penguins. So they crowd and push until they manage to shove one penguin off, to see if it's safe. I mean if he doesn't get eaten up, the rest of them know it's safe for all to jump in.

MRS. POPPER: Dear me! They sound like savage birds to me.

MR. POPPER: It's a queer thing that all the polar bears live at the North Pole and all the penguins are at the South Pole. I should think the penguins would like the North Pole, too, if they only knew how to get there.

MRS. POPPER: Well—you can go on reading about those savage birds, but I'm going to bed. Tomorrow is Thursday, September 30th, and I have to go to the meeting of the Ladies Aid and Missionary Society.

MR. POPPER: September 30th! You don't mean that to-night is Wednesday, September 29th?

MRS. POPPER: Why, yes. I suppose it is—but what of it?

MR. POPPER: Why, this is the night the Drake Antarctic Expedition is going to start broadcasting!

MRS. POPPER: Oh, that's nothing. Just a lot of men at the bottom of the world saying, "Hello, Mama— Hello, Papa."

MR. POPPER [*Turning on radio*]: Sh! Sh!

ADMIRAL DRAKE: This is Admiral Drake speaking—Hello, Mama— Hello, Papa— Hello, Mr. Popper.

MRS. POPPER: Goodness gracious! Did he say—"Papa" or "Popper"?

ADMIRAL DRAKE: Hello, Mr. Popper, up there in Stillwater. Thanks for your nice letter about the picture of our last expedition. Watch for an answer. But not by letter, Mr. Popper. Watch for a surprise. Signing off— Signing off.

MRS. POPPER: You wrote to Admiral Drake?

MR. POPPER: Yes, I did. I wrote and told him how funny I thought the penguins were.

MRS. POPPER: Well, I never!

MR. POPPER: And to think he spoke to me all the way from there—and he even mentioned my name! Mama, what do you suppose he means by a surprise?

MRS. POPPER: I don't know, but I do know I'm going to bed.

The Next Day

MR. POPPER *answers knock on door.*

EXPRESSMAN: Party by the name of Popper live here?

MR. POPPER: That's me.

EXPRESSMAN: Here's a package that's come Air Express all the way from Antarctica. Some journey, I'll say.

MR. POPPER [*Reads*]: Unpack at once. Keep cool.

CAPTAIN COOK: Auk—Auk.

[MR. POPPER *takes* CAPTAIN COOK *out of the box.*]

[CHILDREN *enter—*]

JANIE: Oh, Papa! What's that?

MR. POPPER: It's a South Pole penguin, sent to me by Admiral Drake.

BILL: Look! He's marching. For such a big bird, he takes awfully small steps.

JANIE: And see how his little black coat drags behind him. Looks almost as if it were too big for him.

CAPTAIN COOK: Gook. Gook.

MR. POPPER: Sounds like "Cook." Why, that's it, of course. We'll call him "Cook," "Captain Cook."

MRS. POPPER [*Enters*]: Call who "Captain Cook"?

MR. POPPER: Why, the penguin! I was just saying we'd name him after Captain Cook, the famous English explorer, who made a lot of important discoveries about the Antarctic.

MRS. POPPER: Well, I never!

CAPTAIN COOK: Gook. Gook. Gook. [*Nips at* MRS. POPPER.]

MRS. POPPER: Stop him, Papa! Stop him!

JANIE: Maybe he's hungry.

CAPTAIN COOK: Gook. Gook.

MRS. POPPER: He certainly is cute. I guess I'll have to forgive him for nipping at me.

CAPTAIN COOK: Gook. Gook. [*Bites the icebox door handle.*]

MRS. POPPER: What do you suppose he likes to eat?

MR. POPPER: Let's see. [*Takes food from icebox.*] Now then, Captain Cook, how do you like this?

CAPTAIN COOK: Or-r-r-rh, Or-r-r-rh.

MR. POPPER: That's a penguin's way of saying it's pleased. But we ought to have some sea food for him—canned shrimps —or something.

JANIE: Mama, Papa, see what Captain Cook has done! He's eaten the goldfish.

MRS. POPPER: Bad, bad penguin—had to eat the goldfish. [CAPTAIN COOK *hides in the refrigerator.*]

MR. POPPER: I think that's about the right temperature for him at that. We could let him sleep there at night.

MRS. POPPER: But where will I put the food?

MR. POPPER: We'll have to get another icebox for the food.

JANIE: Look—he's gone to sleep.
[CAPTAIN COOK *snores.*]

MR. POPPER [*Whispering*]: Tomorrow I'll have the icebox department send a man to bore holes in the door for air, and then he can put a handle on the inside of the door so Captain Cook can go in and out as he pleases.

MRS. POPPER: Well, dear me—I never thought we'd have a penguin for a pet.

MR. POPPER: You know, penguins make their nests out of pebbles and stones and I'll just take some ice cubes out of the tray and put them under him so he'll feel more comfortable

Act II
Scene I: *The Next Day*

SERVICE MAN *enters, putting tool box on the floor.*
SERVICE MAN: You don't need no ventilating holes in that

box, mister.

MR. POPPER: It's my icebox—and I want some holes bored in the door. I'll pay for it—and there's one more thing.

SERVICE MAN: Now what. I suppose you want me to make a radio set out of your icebox.

MR. POPPER: No, I want you to put a handle on the inside of the door, so it can be opened from the inside.

SERVICE MAN: That's a fine idea. You want an extra handle on the inside. Sure, sure.

MR. POPPER: Aren't you going to do it for me?

SERVICE MAN: Sure, sure.

MR. POPPER: I thought you were a service man.

SERVICE MAN: I am. That's the first sensible thing you've said yet. I'll fix your extra handle, mister, but while I'm doing it, you sit down on that chair over there, facing me, where I can keep an eye on you.

MR. POPPER: Fair enough.

CAPTAIN COOK [*Enters*]: Ork—Ork— [*Nips at* SERVICE MAN.]

JANIE: What happened, Papa?

MR. POPPER: I had these holes bored so that Captain Cook could get air, and the handle put on the inside so that he can go in and out as he pleases.

Scene II

BILL: Papa, there's a policeman at the back door. Is he going to arrest you?

CAPTAIN COOK: Gook. Gook.

POLICEMAN: Is this 432 Proudfoot Avenue?

MR. POPPER: It is.

POLICEMAN: Well, I guess this is the place, all right. Is that thing yours?

MR. POPPER: Yes, it is.

POLICEMAN: And what do you do for a living?

MR. POPPER: I'm a housepainter—won't you come in?

POLICEMAN: Not unless I have to.

BILL: Look, the policeman is afraid of Captain Cook.

CAPTAIN COOK: Gook. Gook.

POLICEMAN: Can it talk? What is it—a giant parrot?

JANIE: It's a penguin. We keep it for a pet.

POLICEMAN: Well, if it's only a bird—but from the way people are talking—I thought there was a lion loose in here.

BILL: Mama says Papa's hair looks like a lion sometimes.

JANIE: Keep still, Bill.

POLICEMAN: Well, if it's only a bird—I suppose it'll be O.K. if you keep him in a cage.

BILL: We keep him in the icebox.

POLICEMAN: What kind of bird did you say it was?

MR. POPPER: A penguin.

POLICEMAN: Well, you'll have to keep him on a leash— and you'll have to get a license for him, too. He certainly is big enough for a license. Well, good luck to you, Popper. He's kind of a cute little fellow, at that—looks almost human. Good day to you, Popper, and good day to you, too, Mr. Penguin.

Scene III: *Much Later*

JANIE: Poor Captain Cook! He's so sick.

BILL: Yes, he wouldn't play marbles with me.

MR. POPPER: He won't eat a thing, Doctor.

DOCTOR: He's very ill—I'll leave some pills, but I'm afraid it's a hopeless case. Penguins are not made for this climate.

MR. POPPER: There's just one hope, Doctor. I wrote to Dr. Smith about Captain Cook's illness. He is curator of the largest aquarium in the world. I'll read you his letter.—"It is not easy to cure a sick penguin. We, too, have one in our aquarium. It is failing rapidly. I think it is suffering from loneliness, and perhaps that is what is the matter with your Captain Cook. I am therefore shipping you, under separate cover, our penguin. You may keep her—there's just a chance that the birds may get on better."

JANIE: Oh, isn't that wonderful! Let's name her Greta.

MR. POPPER: And maybe we could have some little baby penguins.

Scene IV: *Very Much Later*

MRS. POPPER: I must talk to you, Papa. Come and sit down.

MR. POPPER: Yes, my love, what is on your mind?

MRS. POPPER: Papa, I'm glad to see you having a nice vacation. But, Papa, what are we going to use for money? Of course the penguins have to eat, but I don't know how we are ever going to pay for their food.

MR. POPPER: Is all our money gone?

MRS. POPPER: Almost. Of course, when it's all gone—maybe we could eat the penguins.

MR. POPPER: Oh, no, Mama—you don't mean that!

MRS. POPPER: Well, I don't suppose I'd really enjoy eating them, especially Greta and Isabella.

MR. POPPER: It would break the children's hearts, too. But I've been thinking something over, Mama. Have you ever heard of trained seals acting in theaters?

MRS. POPPER: Of course I've heard of seals. They balance balls on the ends of their noses.

MR. POPPER: Well, why can't there be trained penguins?

MRS. POPPER: Perhaps you're right, Papa.

MR. POPPER: Of course I am, and you can help me train them.

MRS. POPPER: They don't need costumes, anyway. They already have them.

MR. POPPER: And when we get them trained, we'll show them to Mr. Greenbaum. He owns theaters all over the country.

Act III
Scene I: *Mr. Greenbaum's Office*

Penguins file in.

MR. GREENBAUM: Say, what's this all about? It looks like an act.

MR. POPPER: It is an act. It's POPPER'S PERFORMING PENGUINS, DIRECT FROM THE SOUTH POLE.

MR. GREENBAUM: Couldn't we call them Popper's Pink-toed Penguins?

MR. POPPER: No, I'm afraid we couldn't. I don't think they'd like it.

MR. GREENBAUM: All right, show me the act.

JANIE: There's music in it, too. Mama plays the piano.

MR. GREENBAUM: Well, there's the piano. If the act is any good, you've come to the right place. You may begin, madam. But aren't you going to take your gloves off?

MRS. POPPER: Oh, no. I always play with them on.

Penguins do the act

MR. GREENBAUM: Congratulations, Mr. Popper. Your act is a sensation. I'm going to book you in the biggest theaters from coast to coast, and your salary will be $5,000 a week.

Scene II: *A New York Hotel*

MR. POPPER: Well, my love, we certainly had a wonderful tour.

MRS. POPPER: Yes, thousands of miles all over the country.

MR. POPPER: And it was so good for the children to see America.

JANIE: I love sleeping on the train.

BILL: And having our meals on the train, too.

MR. POPPER: We owe it all to our dear penguins. Why, they seem almost like our own children, Mother.

MRS. POPPER: They do indeed, Father. We really have fourteen children, instead of just two.

ADMIRAL DRAKE [*Knocks and enters*]: I am so glad to meet you, at last, Mr. Popper! I am Admiral Drake.

MR. POPPER: Admiral Drake—from the South Pole?

ADMIRAL DRAKE: Yes, the Drake expedition ship returned yesterday. New York gave us a great reception. Last night, at the Mayor's dinner for us, I heard about the wonderful penguin act you have been putting on all over the country. It's amazing. It certainly shows what patience and training can do.

MR. POPPER: Oh, we've enjoyed teaching them things.

ADMIRAL DRAKE: Mr. Popper, you may know that I have explored the North Pole, as well as the South Pole.

MR. POPPER: Oh, yes, I've read all about it.

ADMIRAL DRAKE: You know, those long polar nights get very lonely when you have no pets to play with. Now, nobody knows why there are no penguins at the North Pole. So I'll come to the point, Mr. Popper. Why not let me take these birds of yours to the North Pole and start a race of penguins there.

MR. GREENBAUM [*and* MR. KLEIN] *enter*: Here is Mr. Klein, who owns the Colossal Film Company. He is going to make your fortune. You'll be a poor man no longer, Mr. Popper.

MR. POPPER: I'm not poor. These birds have been earning $5,000 a week for us.

MR. KLEIN: $5,000. Why, that's just pin money. I want to put those birds in the movies, Mr. Popper, and I'll pay you so much money that you and the Missus can live on easy street for the rest of your lives.

MRS. POPPER: I don't want to live on easy street, Papa. I want to go back to Proudfoot Avenue.

ADMIRAL DRAKE: Better consider, Mr. Popper. I can't offer you anything like that.

MR. POPPER: Admiral, you say the men at the North Pole get lonely because they have no penguins?

ADMIRAL: Very lonely.

MR. KLEIN: You will be seen in every picture house in America.

ADMIRAL: Of course, if we succeed in establishing a breed at the North Pole, hundreds of years from now scientists will be calling them the Popper Arctic Penguins.

MR. POPPER: Will you give me a moment to consult with my wife?—Mother, what do you think we should do?

MRS. POPPER: The penguins are really yours, Father, and you must do what you think best.

MR. POPPER: Mr. Klein, I'm afraid I'll have to refuse. I don't believe life in Hollywood would be good for the penguins. Admiral Drake, I am going to give you the birds. In doing this, I am considering the birds first of all. They belong in a cold climate, and I feel sorry for those men at the North Pole without any penguins to help them pass the time.

MR. KLEIN: Congratulations, Admiral. Maybe you're right, Mr. Popper. Hollywood might have been too much for them. Good-by— Good-by—everybody.

MR. POPPER: Life is going to be very lonely for me without my penguins, Admiral.

ADMIRAL: What do you mean, aren't you coming with us?

MR. POPPER: Me, go with you—to the North Pole? Why, how could I go with you? I'm not an explorer—I'm only a housepainter.

ADMIRAL: You're the keeper of the penguins, aren't you? Man alive—those penguins are the reason for this whole expedition! And who is going to see that they're well and happy —if you don't go along? Now, put on one of those fur suits like the rest of us—we're sailing in an hour.

MR. POPPER: Mama, I'm going too! Admiral Drake says

he needs me. Do you mind if I don't come home for a year or two?

MRS. POPPER: Oh, I'll miss you very much, my dear, but it will be easier to keep the house tidy without a man sitting around all day. Now we must get back to Stillwater. Come, children. Good-by, my love— Good-by—and Good Luck. [MR. POPPER *and the penguins march out.*]

Sokar and the Crocodile

ADAPTED FROM THE BOOK BY ALICE HOWARD

BY EMILY ANN BARNES AND BESS M. YOUNG

AND THE SIXTH GRADE AT LINCOLN SCHOOL,

TEACHERS COLLEGE, COLUMBIA UNIVERSITY

Characters

SOKAR-SHINES-WITH-SPIRIT
SOKAR'S FATHER
CROCODILE
SACRED CAT
WISE HERON
PRINCESS HATHOR
QUEEN NEMATHAP
KING ZOSER
GUARDS
SLAVES

Time—About 4000 B.C.
Place—Ancient Egypt

SOKAR AND THE CROCODILE
This play, made from *Sokar and the Crocodile* by Alice Howard, and copyright by Macmillan, 1922, is used with their permission and that of Bess M. Young.

SOKAR AND THE CROCODILE

Sokar and the Crocodile was dramatized by a group of sixth grade children who were studying "Egypt Now and Long Ago."

The setting of the story is during the time of the building of the pyramids, in the Third Dynasty. The verses used in the book were taken from ancient papyri. Even though the story is of a fairy-tale nature, it presents some of the historical aspects of the development of ancient Egypt and has a rich background of traditions and beliefs.

The play, adapted from the story, has a broad appeal. It was presented for the enjoyment of the elementary school from the first through the sixth grades. The entire audience was enthusiastic and appreciated the dramatic treat provided by this sixth grade.

Scene I: Sokar's Wish

Outside the hut where SOKAR *lives.*

SOKAR [*Addressing the Nile*]: Mud and clay! Mud and clay and water! Such a river! You are always changing. In winter you are so small we scarce can see you; in summer you swell and flood most of the village. [*Pauses.*] I should not say that, I suppose, for Father says, "Egypt is the gift of the Nile." [*Kneeling by the river.*] I love you, River Nile. You provide me with food and work. I like to help the fishermen catch their fish, while I listen to the bird catcher's song as he mends the snares. I can hear them singing even now.

With snare in hand I hide me,
I wait and will not stir.
The beauteous birds of Araby
Are perfumed all with myrrh.

[*Dips hands into the river; gazes off stage. Sighs.*] I wish I could live a fairy story. Then I would be a prince or perhaps a king. I would have slaves to wait on me. [*Picks up a clay bowl from the floor.*] I would not have to make clay bowls all the day. They would already be made for me. My slaves would bring me any number of them that I wanted.

[FATHER *comes in from the hut.*]

FATHER: Why are you not working, Sokar, my son? Stop your dreaming. These jars must be done before the Black Boar Set eats the White Moon Pig.

[SOKAR *starts working on the bowl;* FATHER *gathers up the finished bowls and returns to the hut.*]

SOKAR: Father has gone! Here is a chance for a game. I am tired of clay and mud. [*Throws ball of clay and breaks a large bowl which* FATHER *has made.*] What have I done? Oh God Ptah! I must put the pieces back together. [*Tries to fit pieces together.*] I cannot do it. I cannot mend it. What shall I do?

FATHER [*Calling from within*]: Sokar-Shines-With-Spirit! Bring the large jar to me.

[SOKAR *starts to run off stage while his* FATHER *continues to call.*]

SOKAR [*From a distance, crouched behind a tree*]: Where can I hide? I cannot take it to him. I have broken his very best jar. He must not find me. [*Looking around.*] Everything is flat and open here except the papyrus plants along the river. I'll hide there. The papyri are high and they will shield me.

FATHER [*Continues to call as he appears on the stage*]: Sokar! Sokar! What is this? My very best jar is broken! Sokar! Sokar! It could not have been Sokar. [*Continues calling.*] Sokar! Sokar! S-o-k-a-r!

Curtain

Scene II: Sokar's Promise

SOKAR [*Panting*]: What shall I do? I should go home and tell Father what has happened. But that I cannot do. I cannot! [*Hears a rustle in the papyri.*] What is that? Oh, oh! I do hope it is not a crocodile. I am so frightened! How well I remember the story my father told me about a magician who made a wax crocodile and threw it into the water. When a bad man came to bathe, the crocodile became alive and ate him up. What is that? [*Frightened.*] Oh! It *is* a crocodile! Oh! Crocodile, wax or real, please do not eat me. [*To audience.*] I am so frightened. [*To* CROCODILE.] I'll do anything. I'll bring you the Magic Lotus Bud if you will not eat me.

CROCODILE: What good would a Magic Lotus Bud be to me? I'm hungry and I want something to eat. I cannot eat the Magic Lotus Bud. I'm hungry and I want something to eat. Why not eat you? A flower will not feed me.

SOKAR: But if you eat the Magic Lotus Bud, you will turn into a prince.

CROCODILE: Ah, that is different. I should like very much to become a prince. [*Pauses thoughtfully.*] Very well, then; if I spare you now, will you promise to find the Magic Lotus Bud for me? [SOKAR *nods his head.*] Meet me here tomorrow at this time and bring the Magic Lotus Bud with you. I shall be waiting for you. If you do not come, I shall find you wherever you are. [CROCODILE *goes out*; SOKAR *turns to the audience.*]

SOKAR: I promise! I promise! My, but I was frightened! What made me promise to bring the Magic Lotus Bud? I do not know where to find it. I must go in search of it. But where? Where!

Curtain

Scene III: Sokar's Visit
Part I. Outside the QUEEN'S *garden.*

*Same setting as Scene I; reversing hut and wall to form
wall of* QUEEN'S *garden. Trees set close to wall.*

SOKAR: Where is the Magic Lotus Bud? I have looked and
looked for it, but it is not to be found. I am so tired—so
tired. Here I am, outside the Queen's garden. Oh God Ptah,
where can I find the Magic Lotus Bud? Father has told me
about the Egyptian lilies and how they grow in pools and
fountains. The Magic Lotus Bud is sure to be in the royal
pool. Maybe I can find it in there; I might be able to see the
ladies who pull the lilies to twine in their hair. And perhaps
—oh, wonderful—perhaps I may see the Queen herself and
ask her to help me. [*Addressing* UZAT, *the charm around his
neck.*] Oh, Uzat, my pretty little Uzat. Show me where to go.
Tell me what to do. I know you will protect me against all
bad things. Help me now. Good Ptah of White Wall, will you
not help me? I remember the story about your eight little
dwarfs who long ago hammered out the sky of copper and
made the hills and valleys. Surely they would help me to find
the Magic Lotus Bud.
[*Enter* CAT.]

CAT: *Me-i-aou—me-i-aou!* Why do you call on Ptah?
Trouble him not, but call on me, for I am sent to help you.

SOKAR [*Whispering confidently to the audience*]: Ah, the
Sacred Cat of the Temple! I shall ask her. [*Addresses* CAT.]
I am looking for the Magic Lotus Bud. If I do not get it, the
Crocodile will eat me. It is most important that I find the
Magic Lotus Bud, for I do not want to be eaten.

CAT: Of course not. Can you climb? Can you climb a wall?

SOKAR: Oh, yes. I've climbed to the top of the highest palm
trees to get dates. You know that is a long way up. I've
climbed fig trees, too.

CAT: That is good practice and should help you now. First,

you must climb up that tree over there by the wall. In that way, you will get into the Queen's garden. But you must wait until the sun is very hot and the guards are asleep before you enter. In the royal garden are many lotus blossoms, and they are all white. But—in the Queen's own garden, in the center pool, is a rare plant. The blossoms are a beautiful blue, and one of the buds is the Magic Lotus Bud.

SOKAR: But how shall I know it?

CAT: *That* I cannot tell you, little Sokar-Shines-With-Spirit. I cannot go with you, but I shall help you. Take this hair from my tail. If you get into trouble, throw it to the north. Call, "Helpers of Ptah, come!" and help will come. Now climb the wall. Drop into the bushes. Go to the far end of the garden and crawl through the water channel. Wait until the sun is hot and the guards are asleep. Remember the hair from my tail and call on Ptah.

[*Exit* CAT.]

SOKAR: First, I must climb the tree over by the wall. [*Goes slowly toward tree. Curtain closes, leaving impression that he is climbing the wall.*]

Curtain

Scene III: Sokar's Visit
Part II. Inside the QUEEN'S *garden.*

SOKAR *crouched behind a tree near the front of the stage.*

SOKAR: It is so hot and I am so tired! But I must wait. The Sacred Cat told me to wait until the guards are asleep. [GUARDS *begin to droop.*] Ah! they are getting drowsy now. I shall not have to wait much longer. [GUARDS *drop slowly to the floor.*] At last they are asleep! [*Comes from behind tree.*] Here are lotus buds, but where is the magic one? I'll ask the Heron. Oh, Mr. Heron, are you guarding these flowers? Will you not tell me, please, which is the Magic Lotus Bud?

HERON: You'll be sorry! You'll be sorry! But I'll tell you. It's that one. [*Indicates which it is by a nod of the head.*] You'll be sorry! [SOKAR *picks the bud.*]

SOKAR: I have found it at last. Now I can keep my promise to the Crocodile. I must be on my way.

[PRINCESS HATHOR *enters with her attendants.*]

PRINCESS HATHOR: Stop, little boy! I would not go if I were you. No one who comes into this garden ever goes out again. [*Sadly.*] No, they never go out again.

SOKAR: But I *must* go. If I do not give this to the Crocodile, he will eat me.

PRINCESS HATHOR: He cannot eat you if you stay here, for there are no crocodiles in this garden. It is too bad that you picked a blue lotus bud, because the Queen Mother said that whoever did so must die. No one has ever dared to do such a thing before. I must try to help you, little boy.

HERON [*Almost echoing*]: You'll be sorry! You'll be sorry! [*In the distance the* QUEEN MOTHER *claps her hands.*]

PRINCESS HATHOR: Here comes the Queen Mother. Oh, little boy, creep under my chair and hide. She will be so angry when she sees that the blossom has been taken.

[SOKAR *drops the bud as he hides under the chair. The* QUEEN *goes to the pool and in silence examines the buds.*]

QUEEN MOTHER: Someone has been picking my blue lotus flowers. A bud has disappeared. [*Looks around.*] Ah! there it is. It was you. [*Accusing the* PRINCESS.] She shall die! [*To audience.*] I hate her, anyway. This is my chance for revenge. I did not send to the Harbor of Incense for a child like her. She shall not be the future queen if I have anything to do with it.

[SOKAR *jumps from behind the chair.*]

PRINCESS HATHOR: Queen Mother, I—

SOKAR: I did it! I picked it! I needed it! [*Pleading.*] You have so many! Why do you care for one little bud when the pool is filled with them? I promised to take it to the Crocodile.

I must go now.

QUEEN MOTHER: Ha! You shall die because you have picked a blue lotus bud. [QUEEN *calls guards.*] Take him to the dungeon.

[SOKAR *is led off by the* GUARDS *as he calls frantically to the* PRINCESS, *"Save me!"*]

PRINCESS HATHOR: Go! I shall help you if I can!

QUEEN MOTHER [*To the audience*]: Since he is but a little boy, he shall be a slave for life. I shall not kill him. He must serve my purposes. He shall help other slaves to carry the heavy stones to King Zoser's pyramid. [*Looks at lotus plants.*] How dare he pick my lotus buds!

[*The* QUEEN MOTHER *goes out.*]

HERON: You'll be sorry! You'll be sorry!

[SOKAR, *out of breath, rushes into the garden again.*]

PRINCESS HATHOR: How did you get away?

SOKAR: I used the Sacred Cat's hair. Everything happened as it does in a fairy story. The guards fell asleep. Oh, God Ptah, you were kind to me!

PRINCESS HATHOR: I must help you! Perhaps some day, if I am Queen, you can come to the Harbor of Incense. The Queen Mother hates me. What can I do— [*Looking off into the distance, she sees the* KING *coming.*] Here comes the King. He is my friend. I shall tell him what I wish. He will help us!

KING [*Noticing the sadness of the* PRINCESS]: Fair Hathor, you are as fair as a flower, but you look troubled. What favor may I grant you this day to cause you to smile?

PRINCESS HATHOR: Oh, King Zoser, give me this little boy to be my slave and mine only.

KING: So be it. He shall be yours!

[KING *and* ATTENDANTS *go out.*]

PRINCESS HATHOR [*To* SOKAR]: No one can hurt you now. You shall fan me when the days are hot. Tell me your name.

SOKAR: Sokar-Shines-With-Spirit.

PRINCESS HATHOR: What a lovely name! Do not be afraid,

Sokar. Come with me.

SOKAR [*Aside*]: I cannot stay here. I must make her understand that I must go back to the Crocodile. Good Ptah, tell me what to do. Should I stay here with the Princess and be a slave or shall I go back to the Crocodile? [*With determination.*] I will stay.

[QUEEN MOTHER *enters.*]

QUEEN MOTHER: You here! I thought that I sent you to the dungeon.

PRINCESS HATHOR: King Zoser gave him to me for my slave.

QUEEN MOTHER: The King! How dare he disregard my orders!

PRINCESS [*To* SOKAR]: Come, let us go to the palace before she does me harm.

QUEEN MOTHER [*To audience*]: I shall be more cunning next time. I will fix him. I shall have the scribe write a note to the royal builder of the pyramid. He shall use hieratic writing, for I am sure the slave boy will not be able to read it. In the note, I shall tell the builder to use this boy for heavy work. He shall pull and haul stones. The royal builder is a wonderful slave-driver. [*Thoughtfully.*] I shall have the note sealed and then the little slave boy will not know what is in it. He will think that it is merely a message for the builder from King Zoser.

[*The* QUEEN MOTHER *goes out.*]

HERON: They'll be sorry! They'll be sorry!

[SOKAR *and* PRINCESS *come out together,* SOKAR *holding a small scroll of papyrus.*]

PRINCESS HATHOR: Go, Sokar. Take the scroll from the King and carry it to the royal builder.

SOKAR: Should I trust the Queen? God Ptah, be with me.

HERON: You'll be sorry. You'll be sorry!

    Curtain

Scene IV: Sokar's Escape

SLAVE BOY: Come this way. Let us rest, for we are out of his reach at last. Tonight, when the Black Boar Set eats the White Moon Pig, I intend to steal away to Memphis. There I shall become a scribe and sit in the market place. Do you wish to come with me?

SOKAR: No, I cannot go. I must carry this Lotus Bud to the Crocodile or he will find me and eat me.

SLAVE BOY: The Crocodile?

SOKAR: Yes. I ran away from home and had an adventure with a crocodile.

SLAVE BOY: How did you become a slave?

SOKAR: Oh, that hateful old Queen! She sent me with a letter from the King to the royal builder, and I trusted her, thinking that it really was from the King. In the letter she said that I was to be a slave for life because I picked a blue lotus bud from her royal garden. So here I am—sore to the bone—my body covered with welts from the slave-driver's whip. I shall rest a while, so that I may be off when the sun peeps over his golden path. I must carry the Magic Lotus Bud to the Crocodile because I promised to give it to him.

[*Lighting effects to indicate approaching night.*]

SLAVE BOY: Little Sokar-Shines-With-Spirit, rest here in the papyri until the sun peeps over his golden path. I must be off, for you see the Black Boar Set has eaten the White Moon Pig. May God Ra protect you!

SOKAR: May God Ptah protect you for helping me this day!

[*Exit* SLAVE BOY. SOKAR *goes to sleep. Lights slowly come on to show approaching dawn.* SOKAR *awakens.*]

SOKAR: The sun is now peeping over his golden path, and I must be on my way.

[CROCODILE *appears.*]

CROCODILE: Aha! I have found you at last. I went to the

meeting place at sunrise, but you were not there, so I had no breakfast. I went to the palace, but you were not there. I warned you that I would find you wherever you went. What a good breakfast *you* will make, little boy. The very last words you said were, "I promise! I promise!" Where is this Magic Lotus Bud? [*Anxiously.*] I shall eat you, for I am very, very hungry.

SOKAR: No, no, no! You shall *not* eat me for I have found the Magic Lotus Bud. Here it is, Mr. Crocodile. Close your eyes and I shall throw it into your mouth. [*Aside.*] Now we shall see if it is really magic.

[*Lights go off and come on again suddenly.* CROCODILE *draws back into the wings of the stage and* PRINCE *appears.*]

PRINCE: Who am I?

SOKAR: Don't you remember, Mr. Crocodile, about the Magic Lotus Bud?

PRINCE: Mr. Crocodile? Magic Lotus Bud? I seem to remember. I lived in a palace with tall columns. [*Thoughtfully.*] It seems that I should have been a king.

SOKAR: That sounds like a fairy tale.

PRINCE: A cruel magician changed me into a crocodile and doomed me to wander until I was saved by a slave child. Now I see everything. *You* are the little child; the Lotus Bud was magic. I'm so glad that I did not eat you, for now the spell of the magician has been broken. I am a prince, who shall become a king.

[*Enter the* HERON.]

SOKAR: How strange! How came the Heron from the Queen's garden?

HERON: She pulled my tail feathers, the Queen did. She said I was a spy. She hates the Princess and was planning to kill her because she wept for you, Sokar. The Queen thought she was alone in the garden, but I overheard her say, "A drop of this in her alabaster cup and she dies." I could not help but say, "You'll be sorry! You'll be sorry!" She seized

me and said, "You spy!" Then she pulled out my most beautiful feathers, and I came away. [*Pleading.*] Oh, Sokar-Shines-
With-Spirit, please save the Princess.

SOKAR: God Ptah of White Wall, save the Princess.

[CAT *enters with the* PRINCESS HATHOR.]

CAT: *Me-i-aou! Me-i-aou!*

SOKAR: Why, here is the Sacred Cat, and how wonderful
of her to bring the Princess Hathor with her. Prince Croco,
this is the Princess who was so kind to me in the Queen's
garden.

PRINCE: Princess Hathor, it seems to me that I have met
you before. Did you not come from the Harbor of Incense?

PRINCESS HATHOR: Indeed, yes. And who are you?

PRINCE: I am Prince Croco.

PRINCESS HATHOR: Is this not strange? I feel that I have
known you always.

PRINCE: Would it not be wonderful for us to go together
to that far-off land—to the Harbor of Incense?

[SOKAR *walks away weeping.*]

PRINCESS HATHOR [*Goes towards* SOKAR]: Why do you
weep, little boy? Are you not always to be happy and free?

SOKAR: Yes, Princess Hathor, but I feel somehow that a
great fairy story is about to come to an end.

[*Off stage a voice calls,* "Sokar." FATHER *enters.*]

FATHER: Sokar—Sokar-Shines-With-Spirit!

PRINCE: Who can *this* be?

SOKAR: This is my father. He is angry with me because I
broke his jar and ran away. Oh, Prince Croco, *do* protect me.

FATHER: Sokar! Just today I carried an offering to the
gods so that they might send you back to me.

SOKAR: Father, this is Prince Croco and Princess Hathor.
They have been so kind to me and have promised to protect
me. Would it not be wonderful to live with them always?
Then neither you nor I would have to make another jar or
work again so long as we live.

PRINCE: Jar? Work?

FATHER [*To* PRINCE]: I am a maker of jars that are sent to the far ends of the earth. All people know me by my work.

PRINCE: Why, you are the maker of those wonderful jars which are sought even in the Harbor of Incense, far, far away! Will you and Sokar come with the Princess and me to the Land of Wonders? I need a man to make such jars for me and the Princess wants Sokar-Shines-With-Spirit with her always. You will become rich in a land where I am king.

SOKAR: Please let's go, Father.

FATHER: I shall go anywhere, if Sokar is only there.

PRINCE: Oh, God Ptah, send us the Golden Boat, so that we may be on our way to the Harbor of Incense.

[CAT *takes a hair from his tail and calls on God Ptah.*]

CAT: *Me-i-aou! Me-iou!* Here comes the Golden Boat! [*Golden Boat is pushed slowly on the stage.*] *Me-i-aou! Me-i-aou!*

PRINCE: Sacred Cat tells us to be on our way. Come, let us be off to the Harbor of Incense, to the Land of Wonder.

HERON: You will be happy! You will be happy!

[*Continues calling "You will be happy," until the curtains close.*]

*   *   *

PRODUCTION NOTES

The illustrations in the book, *Sokar and the Crocodile,* are in black and white and are the work of the artist Coleman Kubinyi. The publishers have also introduced a few simple drawings by ten-year-old children. These are instructive to the reader and very suggestive of possibilities for scenery and costuming.

Also consult books on historical costumes and the history of Egypt.

The Magic Fishbone

ADAPTED FROM THE BOOK BY CHARLES DICKENS

BY EMILY ANN BARNES AND BESS M. YOUNG

AND THE SIXTH GRADE AT LINCOLN SCHOOL,

TEACHERS COLLEGE, COLUMBIA UNIVERSITY

Characters

KING WATKINS THE FIRST

PRINCESS ALICIA

THE QUEEN

MR. PICKLES (*Fishmonger*)

MR. PICKLES' BOY

THE DUCHESS

FAIRY GRANDMARINA

PRINCE CERTAINPERSONIO

THE MAGIC FISHBONE
Used with the permission of Bess M. Young.

THE MAGIC FISHBONE

The Magic Fishbone is one of Charles Dickens' simplest and most childlike stories. The plot is presented on a level with the interests of fifth- and sixth-grade children, thus the story can be thoroughly enjoyed and appreciated by them.

This story is one of four written by Dickens in 1861. It was published in *Our Young Folks Magazine* under the title, "A Holiday Romance." Dickens pretended that children had written these tales. This may be the reason why *The Magic Fishbone* has such a natural, childlike appeal and can be read and enjoyed as much as any of the modern types of fiction and adventure read by children.

The Magic Fishbone was the "Romance from the pen of Miss Alice Rainbird, age six." Dickens wrote in a letter to his publisher, "I hope it (the story) is droll and childlike, though the joke is a grown-up one."

The class which wrote and produced this play was so enthusiastic about the story that the boys and girls wanted to know more about the author and to become familiar with his other writings.

There are no production notes or suggestions for costumes except those at the beginning of the play. The illustrations from the several editions of the story would be helpful in planning scenes, settings and costumes.

A WORD BEFORE

Once upon a time there was a King whose wife was a Queen. Of all men he was the manliest; of all women she was the fairest. In private life, the King followed a profession. He was under government. The Queen was the daughter of a medical man out-of-town.

Nineteen children had the King and Queen, but ever so often they had more. It required seventeen of the children to take care of the baby, but Alicia, the eldest, took care of them all. Their ages ranged and varied from seven years to seven months. Now let us resume the story.

Scene I: *At the Fishmonger's*

Curtain opens, and MR. PICKLES *is seen behind the counter, counting his money. Above him is a sign:* MR. PICKLES, THE FISHMONGER. *Near him is his son, mopping the floor violently. An old lady, dressed in shot silk of the richest quality, smelling of dried lavender, comes trotting up. Just then* KING WATKINS THE FIRST *enters the shop.*

FAIRY GRANDMARINA [*Talking to* MR. PICKLES' BOY]: Ah, you know me, my lad, but notice, the King does not.
[MR. PICKLES' BOY *nods his head.*]

KING WATKINS THE FIRST: Good morning, Mr. Pickles. May I have a pound of salmon, the very best salmon, not too near the tail?

MR. PICKLES: Certainly, sir. Is there anything else I can do for you, sir?

KING WATKINS THE FIRST: No, I think not, but remember, not too near the tail.
[*The* KING *walks out in a melancholy mood.*]

Curtain

Scene II: *The King on His Way to the Office*

KING WATKINS THE FIRST [*Walking*]: Ah me! I wish quarter day would come. The children are outgrowing their clothes, and we are so poor.

MR. PICKLES' BOY [*Running*]: Sir! You did not see the old

lady in our shop?

KING WATKINS THE FIRST: What old lady? I saw none.

MR. PICKLES' BOY: Why, the good Fairy Grandmarina.

KING WATKINS THE FIRST: Fairies? Phew!

MR. PICKLES' BOY [*Spying the* FAIRY]: Here she comes now.

FAIRY GRANDMARINA: King Watkins the First, I believe?

KING WATKINS THE FIRST: Watkins is my name.

FAIRY GRANDMARINA: Father of the beautiful Princess Alicia?

KING WATKINS THE FIRST: And of eighteen other darlings.

FAIRY GRANDMARINA: Listen, you are going to the office.

KING WATKINS THE FIRST [*Aside to the audience*]: She must be a fairy, she knows that I am going to the office.

FAIRY GRANDMARINA: I *am* a fairy.

KING WATKINS THE FIRST [*Aside to the audience*]: She is a fairy, she even knows what I thought.

FAIRY GRANDMARINA: Attend! When you arrive at home to-night, politely invite the beautiful Princess Alicia to partake of the salmon you have just bought.

KING WATKINS THE FIRST: But it might disagree with her.

FAIRY GRANDMARINA [*Angrily*]: This thing disagreeing, and that thing disagreeing. Hoity toity me! Don't be greedy. I believe you want it all yourself.

KING WATKINS THE FIRST: I'm sorry, Fairy Grandmarina, and I won't talk about things disagreeing any more.

FAIRY GRANDMARINA: Be good then, and don't! When beautiful Princess Alicia consents to partake of the salmon, as I think she will, you will find that she leaves a fishbone on her plate. Tell her to dry it and rub it and polish it till it shines like mother-of-pearl, and to keep it as a present from me.

KING WATKINS THE FIRST: Is that all?

FAIRY GRANDMARINA: Don't be impatient, sir! Don't catch people short before they are done speaking. Tell her that it is a *magic fishbone* and that it will bring her whatever she wishes for, provided she wishes for it at the right time.

KING WATKINS THE FIRST: May I ask the reason?

FAIRY GRANDMARINA: Will you be good? You grown-ups with all your reasons! The reason for this and the reason for that! There is no reason. There!

KING WATKINS THE FIRST: I shall not ask for reasons any more.

FAIRY GRANDMARINA: Be good then, and don't. Now that I have told you the message, will you please tell it to me?

KING WATKINS THE FIRST [*Answering hesitatingly*]: I . . . to tell the Princess Alicia to t . . . ake some of the f . . . ish I . . . have just bought, and . . . the fishbone she leaves on her plate, I am to tell her to . . .

FAIRY GRANDMARINA: So, you have forgotten the most important part!

KING WATKINS THE FIRST: No, no, I am to tell her to dry it and rub it and polish it till it shines like mother-of-pearl, and to keep it as a present from you. It is a magic fishbone; she can wish but once and it will bring her whatever she wishes for, providing she wishes at the right time.

FAIRY GRANDMARINA [*Waving her fan haughtily*]: Very good, sir. Be gone!

   Curtain

Scene III: *In the King's Dining Room*

The KING, QUEEN, *and* ALICIA *are eating their meal.*

KING WATKINS THE FIRST: I had a wonderful happening today.

ALICIA: What was it, Father?

KING WATKINS THE FIRST: I met a fairy.

ALICIA: Oh! a fairy? Was she pretty? Please tell me more about her, Father.

KING WATKINS THE FIRST [*To* QUEEN]: My dear wife, won't you have some fish? Oh, but I cannot help thinking of quarter day.

QUEEN: Don't bother me about quarter day. I feel ill.

ALICIA: Oh, Mother!

KING WATKINS THE FIRST [*To* ALICIA]: The fairy gave me a message for you.

ALICIA: For me, Father? What was the message?

KING WATKINS THE FIRST [*Turning to audience*]: She took the fish and left the fishbone, just as the fairy said she would. [*Turning to* ALICIA.] She said that you should take the fishbone that you have left on your plate and that you should dry it and rub it and polish it till it shines like mother-of-pearl, and keep it as a present from her. It will bring you whatever you wish for, provided you wish for it at the right time.

ALICIA: How wonderful, Father! If you ever see that good fairy again, tell her that I shall dry it and rub it and polish it till it shines like mother-of-pearl and that I shall not use it too soon.

[KING WATKINS THE FIRST *smiles and offers some salmon to the* QUEEN.]

QUEEN: I don't care for any salmon. I feel quite faint.

ALICIA: Oh, Mother, do you really?

[QUEEN *nods weakly. The* KING *and* ALICIA *are alarmed.* ALICIA *helps the poor* QUEEN *out.*]

    Curtain

Scene IV: *In the King's Study*

    The KING *is seated at his desk.*

KING WATKINS THE FIRST [*To himself*]: When will quarter day ever come?

[ALICIA *enters.*]

ALICIA: Father, Mother is so very ill.

KING WATKINS THE FIRST: Where is the magic fishbone, Alicia?

ALICIA: In my pocket, Father.

KING WATKINS THE FIRST: I thought you had lost it.

ALICIA: Oh, no, Father.

KING WATKINS THE FIRST: Or forgotten it.

ALICIA: No, indeed, Father.

KING WATKINS THE FIRST: Well, you'll have to attend to her yourself, Alicia.

[ALICIA *runs to the duchess, her doll.*]

ALICIA [*Taking the duchess in her arms*]: Duchess, my dear, shall I use the magic fishbone? Mother is very ill; the children are noisy and very hard to care for. You shake your head. Well, I suppose you are right. Good-by, dear.

[ALICIA *goes off stage.*]

KING WATKINS THE FIRST [*Walking about restlessly*]: Why does not Alicia wish? The children all need new shoes and stockings, too.

ALICIA [*Comes in, holding a small child by the hand*]: Father!

KING WATKINS THE FIRST: What is it now, Alicia?

ALICIA: Father, the baby fell under the grate. The other little princes and princesses are quite used to falling under the grate, but the baby is not. See, Father, it gave the poor little dear a swelled face and a black eye.

KING WATKINS THE FIRST: Where is the magic fishbone, Alicia?

ALICIA: In my pocket, Father.

KING WATKINS THE FIRST: I thought you had lost it.

ALICIA: Oh, no, Father.

KING WATKINS THE FIRST: Or forgotten it.

ALICIA: No, indeed, Father.

KING WATKINS THE FIRST: Well, I guess you had better take her to the cook.

ALICIA: But, Father, the cook has run away with a tipsy-topsy soldier, just at the time when we need her most.

KING WATKINS THE FIRST: Oh, gracious, Alicia, do not bother me any more. [ALICIA *then takes the* BABY *away.*]

KING WATKINS THE FIRST [*In a dejected tone*]: What is the

use of a magic fishbone without a wish? I don't think that I believe in fairies, after all.

ALICIA [*Comes in again with one of the* PRINCES]: Father!

KING WATKINS THE FIRST [*Angrily*]: What next, Alicia?

ALICIA: Father, a dreadful little snapping pug-dog, next door, made a rush at one of the young princes as he stood on the steps and terrified him out of his wits, and the prince ran his hand through a broken pane of glass, and it bled, and it bled, and it bled. See, Father!

[ALICIA *shows the bleeding hand of the little* PRINCE *to her* FATHER.]

KING WATKINS THE FIRST: Alicia?

ALICIA: Yes, Father.

KING WATKINS THE FIRST: What has become of the magic fishbone?

ALICIA: It is in my pocket, Father.

KING WATKINS THE FIRST: I thought you had lost it.

ALICIA: Oh, no, Father.

KING WATKINS THE FIRST: Or forgotten it.

ALICIA: No, indeed, Father.

KING WATKINS THE FIRST: Well, I'm sure I do not know what you are to do.

[ALICIA *goes to the duchess.*]

ALICIA: Oh, duchess, the baby fell under the grate and the young prince got a black eye, and was frightened by a pug-dog next door and cut his hand badly on a pane of glass. Shall I use the magic fishbone? Well, I suppose you are right; I had better wait. You dear, sweet thing. I love you.

Curtain

Scene V: *The Same*

ALICIA *is seen sewing. The fishbone is behind her on the sofa. The* KING *enters and sees the fishbone. He picks it up and looks at it wistfully.*

KING WATKINS THE FIRST: Ah, if I could only wish, I know what I would wish! I would wish for quarter day to come, but I suppose it is not for me to wish. [*Aloud.*] Alicia, what are you doing?

ALICIA [*Turning and taking the fishbone quickly*]: Snipping, stitching, cutting, and contriving, Father.

KING WATKINS THE FIRST: What else are you doing, Alicia?

ALICIA: Keeping the children light-hearted, Father.

KING WATKINS THE FIRST: Where is the magic fishbone, Alicia?

ALICIA: In my pocket, Father.

KING WATKINS THE FIRST: I thought you had lost it.

ALICIA: Oh, no, Father.

KING WATKINS THE FIRST: Or forgotten it.

ALICIA: No, indeed, Father.

[KING *heaves a sigh and goes sadly to his chair.*]

ALICIA: What is the matter, Father?

KING WATKINS THE FIRST: We are dreadfully poor, my child.

ALICIA: Have you no money at all, Father?

KING WATKINS THE FIRST: None, my child.

ALICIA: Is there no way of getting any, Father?

KING WATKINS THE FIRST: No way. I have tried very hard, and I have tried all ways.

ALICIA: Father, when we have tried very hard and have tried all ways, we must have done our very best.

KING WATKINS THE FIRST: Undoubtedly, Alicia.

ALICIA: When we have done our very best, Father, and that isn't enough, I think the right time has come for asking help of others. Let me think! [ALICIA *leaves the room to consult the duchess, and the* KING *becomes quite excited.*]

ALICIA [*Entering and talking to the duchess*]: Duchess, has the time come to use the fishbone? Father has no money and we are very poor. Yes, you are right. I shall wish now. [*Kissing the magic fishbone.*] I WISH THAT QUARTER

DAY WOULD COME!

[*Instantly, money comes flying in from every direction. The* KING *nearly falls off his chair in his excitement. In this confusion, who should come in but the* FAIRY GRANDMARINA *and* MR. PICKLES' BOY! *Both are dressed gorgeously.*]

FAIRY GRANDMARINA: How do you do, Alicia, my dear? I hope I see you pretty well. Give me a kiss.

ALICIA [*Kissing her*]: Oh! Are you the good Fairy Grandmarina?

FAIRY GRANDMARINA [*Turning to the* KING]: Have you been good, sir?

KING WATKINS THE FIRST: I hope so, Fairy Grandmarina.

FAIRY GRANDMARINA [*Turning to* ALICIA]: Now, you know why the Princess Alicia here did not use the magic fishbone sooner.

KING WATKINS THE FIRST: Yes, I do, my dear Fairy.

FAIRY GRANDMARINA: But you did not know then.

KING WATKINS THE FIRST: No, I did not.

FAIRY GRANDMARINA: Any more reasons to ask for?

KING WATKINS THE FIRST: No, Fairy Grandmarina—no more reasons.

FAIRY GRANDMARINA: Be good then. [*Turning to* ALICIA.] You, my dear, go to your dressing room where you will dress for your wedding. You are to marry Prince Certainpersonio. [*Turning to the* KING.] You, go to the Queen and prepare for the wedding. We shall all meet at the church.

KING WATKINS THE FIRST: A wedding! Why . . . a . . .

FAIRY GRANDMARINA: Be careful, sir, are you asking a reason?

Curtain

Scene VI: *After the Wedding*

All march in, crossing the stage from right to left. FAIRY GRANDMARINA *leads, followed by* MR. PICKLES' BOY,

ALICIA *and* PRINCE, KING *and* QUEEN, *the* CHILDREN, *and finally* MR. PICKLES. *As they come back to center, the* FAIRY *faces them.*

FAIRY GRANDMARINA: Now that you are united, my dears, I am sure you would like to know about your future; but first, I must tell the King that there will not be four quarter days a year in the future.

KING WATKINS THE FIRST: Oh, but Fairy Grandmarina!

FAIRY GRANDMARINA [*Smiling*]: But there will be eight, excepting in leap year.

KING WATKINS THE FIRST [*Anxiously*]: But, my dear fairy—

FAIRY GRANDMARINA: Be careful! Are you about to ask for reasons? I said that there will be eight quarter days, and in leap year there will be ten!

KING WATKINS THE FIRST [*Delighted*]: Oh, you wonderful fairy!

FAIRY GRANDMARINA [*Turning to* PRINCESS ALICIA]: You will have thirty-five children—seventeen boys and eighteen girls. The hair of all your children will curl naturally. They will never have the measles, and will have recovered from the whooping cough before they are born.

ALL [*In chorus*]: HIP, HIP, HOORAY!! FAIRY GRAND-MARINA!

[*When the curtain is closing, they can be seen dancing around the good* FAIRY GRANDMARINA.]

> *Curtain*

A WORD AFTER

If you would like to know what has happened to the magic fishbone, I shall tell you. Princess Alicia took it and threw it at the naughty little snapping pug-dog next door that made the little prince's hand bleed. The naughty little dog choked over it and died.

That was the end of the MAGIC FISHBONE.

Ali Baba and the Forty Thieves

BY MURIEL WALZER KLEIN

AND HER SIXTH GRADE AT PLANDOME ROAD SCHOOL,

MANHASSET, N. Y.

Characters

SCHEHERAZADE

HER DANCING ATTENDANTS (2)

SULTAN

DUNYUZAD, *little sister of Scheherazade*

ALI BABA, *a poor woodchopper*

WIFE OF ALI BABA

KASSIM, *rich brother of Ali Baba*

WIFE OF KASSIM

KEREZAN, *son of Ali Baba*

MORJEANEH, *a beautiful slave girl* ⎫
MIRYAN, *another slave girl*   ⎬ *Servants in the house of Ali Baba when he becomes rich*
ZAIDEH, *man house servant*   ⎭

BABA MUSTAPHA, *a cobbler*

CAPTAIN SESAMAUL, *leader of Band of Thieves*

ABOU HASSAM, *a thief*

JAMAL, *a thief*

FIRST THIEF   ⎫
SECOND THIEF ⎬ *other members of band*
THIRD THIEF   ⎭

MEELING   ⎫
TEELING   ⎬ *narrators for Prologue and Epilogue*

ALI BABA AND THE FORTY THIEVES
Used with the permission of Muriel Walzer Klein

ALI BABA AND THE FORTY THIEVES

The Arabian Nights go far back into history. At the time the stories were first written down by a Frenchman, in the eighteenth century, it was thought that they came from Persia. It is now known that they came from many nations in the Eastern world—China, India, Arabia, Persia and North Africa.

Scheherazade was the daughter of the Grande Vizier. She knew the history and literature of her country and was a very clever storyteller. Her father had the unpleasant duty of finding wives for the Sultan, who had each wife killed the day after he married her. Scheherazade thought of a scheme to save the women of Persia from this awful fate. She offered herself as a wife for the Sultan. Her sister was present at the court the first night and asked Scheherazade for a story. Scheherazade began telling an exciting story which was not finished when morning came, so the Sultan let her live another day to finish it. The next night she started another story which was not finished and so it went for "a thousand and one nights." In the meantime, the Sultan had fallen in love with Scheherazade.

"Ali Baba and the Forty Thieves," "Aladdin and His Lamp," and "Sinbad the Sailor" are the most popular of the stories from *The Arabian Nights.* Preadolescent children love the color, drama, excitement, mystery and magic of these Oriental tales.

Prologue

MEELING *and* TEELING *enter, cross stage in front of curtain, bow to each other—then to audience.*

MEELING: Greetings to all and Praises from Allah.

TEELING: We want to take you to a faraway land of fantasy.

MEELING: Where the wicked are cruel and mean

TEELING: And the good are beautiful and kind.

MEELING: This is the story from *The Arabian Nights*

TEELING: Written long years ago, but still enjoyed today.

MEELING: There was in ancient times, in a country between China and India . . .

TEELING: A young girl who had read a thousand books.

MEELING: Her memory was filled with all types of stories of enchantment.

TEELING: Her name was Scheherazade.

MEELING: This is the tale she told of Ali Baba and the Forty Thieves.

TEELING ⎱
MEELING ⎰ : Let's open the curtains to this land of magic.

[*Each pulls curtain as it slowly opens.*]

Scene I: The Sultan's Palace

SULTAN *is seated on throne to one side of stage.* DUNYUZAD *is on footstool near him.*

MILITARY GUARD: Your Majesty, Scheherazade and her handmaidens are ready with their dance.

SULTAN: Let the music begin. [SCHEHERAZADE *and* ATTENDANTS *enter and perform Oriental style of dance. Then* ATTENDANTS *leave.*]

DUNYUZAD: That was beautiful!

SULTAN: Yes, Scheherazade, your dance was very nice. What story will you tell us this evening?

SCHEHERAZADE: Tonight I will tell you the story of Ali Baba and the Forty Thieves.

SULTAN: Let us move to more comfortable quarters. [*Exit from stage to platform on right of audience as curtain closes. Platform is set with colorful cushions in front of large mural of Oriental style window looking out on roof tops of Persian city. Whenever* SCHEHERAZADE *continues her story throughout the play, a spotlight is thrown on this setting, until the action again takes place on stage.*]

SCHEHERAZADE: Come here, little sister, and sit at my feet. Long ago, in a city of Persia, there lived a poor woodcutter named Ali Baba. . . .

Scene II: Robbers' Cave

Scene opens as ALI BABA *enters from left, loading wood, in front of curtain. To the left of the stage, on auditorium floor, is an artificial group of trees, behind which* ALI BABA *can hide.*

ALI BABA: Alas, I wish I were more like my brother, Kassim, who does not have to chop wood for a living. He has married a rich widow who has given him a life of ease. [*Suddenly turns.*] What is that? I hear something. [ALI BABA *leaves and hides behind painted trees, off to left of stage, on auditorium floor.*]

[THIEVES *enter in front of curtain with much noise.* CAPTAIN SESAMAUL, *a tall, dashing-looking thief with bright jewels in his turban, is wearing fine clothing. The two* THIEVES *with him are carrying heavy treasure chests.* CAPTAIN *walks up to center of curtain and speaks.*]

CAPTAIN: Open Sesame. [*Clash of cymbals.*] [*Men go behind curtain.* CAPTAIN *is last to leave. As he goes, one can hear him say*]: Put the gold in the empty wine kegs. [*All disappear behind the curtain.*]

ALI BABA [*Comes out from behind the trees very cautiously*]: Praise be to Allah! What happened? Where did they go? All that the leader said was "Open Sesame" and the heavy rock moved and revealed a passageway. I will wait until they are gone and then I will try this weird magic. [*Noise is heard— men appear.*] Here they come! I hope they do not see my donkeys hidden in the thicket. [*Hides again behind painted trees off to left of stage, watches as* THIEVES *reappear in front of closed curtain*.]

CAPTAIN: Hurry, men, if we are to get to the Turkish Caravan before it reaches the city. [*Exit the way they had entered the auditorium*.]

ALI BABA [*He walks up to center of stage, in front of curtain and says*]: I must try these special words and see what is hidden behind these rocks. Open Sesame! [*Clash of cymbals*.] [*Curtain opens on dimly-lit cave, filled with magnificent wealth. One sees bags of gold, jars overflowing with ropes of pearls and jewelry*.]

ALI BABA: There is so much treasure in this cave! The robbers must have been using it for generations. All this gold! Jewels, emeralds, rubies, diamonds. There is more wealth here than in the Sultan's palaces. [*He walks about, touching the gold, holding up the jewels to see them better*.] Magnificent! I never dreamed such wealth could exist. Praise be to the Creator, now my wife and I shall be vastly richer than my brother, Kassim. [*Runs about, filling his pockets with jewelry, puts bags of gold into his arms*.] I will tell no one but my devoted wife. Open Sesame! [*Clash of cymbals*.] [*Curtains close behind him as he exits the way he had come in, to the left of the stage behind trees*.]

Scene III: Home of Ali Baba

ALI BABA'S *home is simply furnished with dull-colored screen, plain tablecloth on low table.* WIFE *is busy preparing supper.*

WIFE: Where is my poor husband, Ali Baba? I fear the evil spirits of the forest might have brought him harm. He is always home by prayer time— [*Pause*.] Praise be, I think I hear Ali Baba. [*He enters, loaded down with the treasures*.] What troubles came into your path, O beloved husband, that brought you home so late?

ALI BABA: You are very wrong, my dear. Fortune has smiled upon us and showered us with great riches. [*Opens the bags so she can see the jewels he has brought.*]

WIFE [*Gasps*]: Where did you get this? [*Stammers.*] So many pieces of gold are in those bags. Let us count them!

ALI BABA: Count them! It would take all night.

WIFE: I know what we can do. We will borrow the measuring pitcher from your brother Kassim's house and measure the gold.

ALI BABA: That is indeed a fine idea. While you are gone I will take out some of the bricks from the floor and dig a hole so we can bury our treasure, once we have counted the gold pieces. It is best that we keep our good fortune a secret. Do not tell Kassim or his wife about our good luck.

WIFE: I will just tell them I wish to borrow their measuring pitcher.

ALI BABA: Hurry!

Curtain

Scene IV: Home of Kassim

This home is more lavishly furnished than ALI BABA'S. KASSIM'S WIFE *is setting an elaborate table. The dull-colored screens are turned around so that a richly-colored side is visible. The low seats have gay-colored cushions on them. A painted window, hanging on the back stage curtains, shows roof tops of Persian style architecture.*

ALI BABA'S WIFE: Good morning, dear sister-in-law. Oh, and it is an especially beautiful morning.

KASSIM'S WIFE: My, you are in good spirits today!

ALI BABA'S WIFE: We wish to thank you for lending us your measuring pitcher. I made sure to return it this early in case you have need of it. Thank you very much. [*Places pitcher on table.* KASSIM'S WIFE *walks to door with her and waves good-by.*]

KASSIM'S WIFE [*Walks to table*]: I thought she would never leave. I put butter on the bottom of the pitcher to see what they were measuring. [*Lifts up measure.*] Oh, gold! Gold! What! Has Ali Baba gold so plentiful as to measure it? Whence has he all this wealth? [*Calls offstage left.*] Kassim, wake up. Hurry! Hmph, Ali Baba always complaining about how poor he is, barely able to make a living as a woodchopper. Here, he spends half the night, not counting, but measuring gold! I thought we were rich, but we never have had that much gold.

KASSIM [*Enters*]: Is it time to eat? Why must I hurry so?

KASSIM'S WIFE: I know you think yourself rich, but Ali Baba is infinitely richer than you. He does not count his money but has to measure it!

KASSIM: Woman, how can you say such foolish things?

KASSIM'S WIFE: Last night, do you remember when Ali Baba's wife came to borrow a measure?

KASSIM: Yes, yes, go on—

KASSIM'S WIFE: Your very brilliant wife had a splendid idea.

KASSIM [*Aside*]: Nosey wife—go on—

KASSIM'S WIFE: Well, I was curious to find out what kind of grain they were measuring. They always have had so little to eat, but why did they need the measure? So—I put a little butter on the bottom of the measuring pitcher. This morning, much to my amazement when Ali Baba's wife returned it, I found these stuck to the bottom. [*Hands him 3 gold coins.*]

KASSIM: Gold coins! In Allah's name, where did my brother find such wealth?

KASSIM'S WIFE: Go quickly, and find out where he found such treasure. Certainly, Ali Baba would want to share his riches with his only brother. [*Looks out window.*] There is Ali Baba, getting water from the well. Call him in!

KASSIM [*Quickly goes to door and calls*]: Ali Baba, come

into our house.

ALI BABA [*Enters*]: Good morning. 'Tis a fine day.

KASSIM: I am surprised at you. You, Ali Baba, pretend to be miserably poor and yet you measure gold. My wife found these gold coins at the bottom of the measuring pitcher you borrowed last night.

ALI BABA: What, you would stoop so low as to spy on what I measure?

KASSIM: It may be true that my wife and I have not been too concerned with your poor fortune, but now that you are rich, certainly, you would not deprive your own dear brother of knowing how you found such great wealth.

ALI BABA: But, Brother, you have lived in splendor all these years. Surely you are not jealous of my good fortune!

KASSIM: Ali Baba, it would not be well for you to deny me the right to know how you found such riches. I must be told exactly where this treasure is and how I may visit it myself when I choose.

ALI BABA [*Shakes head*]: No, this is my secret.

KASSIM: Otherwise, I will inform against you and then you will not only get no more, but you will lose all you have and I will receive a reward for informing against you.

ALI BABA: Well, although you have not been kind or generous to me and my family, Kassim, I have found such vast treasure I could not possibly use it all up in two lifetimes. There is more than enough for generations of our family. I will share with you my secret. Promise you will never reveal what I tell you.

KASSIM: In Allah's name, I promise to keep your secret.

ALI BABA: Now listen carefully. At the edge of the forest, where I go to cut wood each day, there are two large rocks. Yesterday afternoon, as I was loading the donkeys with wood . . .

Curtain Closes

Scene V: Robbers' Cave

KASSIM *enters from right, in front of curtain. Looks at painted trees to left of stage.*

KASSIM: This must be the tree Ali Baba told me about. Now, six steps straight ahead—one, two, three, four, five, six, then turn left. This must be it. [*Stops at center of stage, in front of curtain.*] I do hope Ali Baba has told me the truth. Now what are the magic words? 'Twas a type of grain. Ah, yes, Open Sesame! [*Clash of cymbals. Curtain slowly opens.*]

KASSIM: Why, it is working! [*He enters the cave.*] Bags of gold! So many silver pieces! It is unbelievable! [*He runs wildly about the cave, pulling out jewelry, stuffing it into his pockets, then, seeing something he thinks looks more valuable, puts it into his pockets and throws away what he had taken previously.*] Ali Baba is such a fool. He brought only three mules and I brought ten. I have never dreamed of such wealth. [*Piles up treasure into middle of the floor.*] What's happening, the door is closing? Why am I worrying? I know the magic words. It is a grain—but what is the word? Let me see—Open Barley! Open Rye! Open Caraway! I've forgotten the magic words! Allah help me! Forgive me for my sins!

[*Curtain closes as cymbals clash. Horses' hoofs heard off stage.*]

[THIEVES *enter by marching down main aisle of auditorium to center of stage. Each member of the* BAND *is carrying different kinds of plunder in sacks, jars and chests. They are colorfully dressed, wear curved swords in their bright sashes and turbans on their heads. One thief has a patch over one eye; many wear large earrings. As they line up in front of the curtain, facing audience, they put their plunder down and turn to look at their* CAPTAIN, *who has taken his place in the middle of the group. He steps forward and begins "The Thieves' Song." See music on opposite page.*]

Bravest Sesamaul (Thieves' Song)

Glenn Weissenberger - Fay Axtell

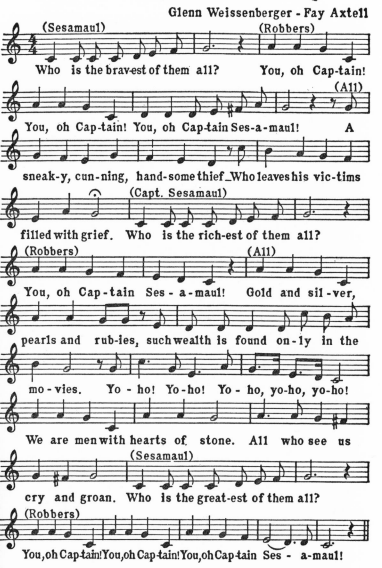

(Sesamaul)
Who is the brav-est of them all?

(Robbers)
You, oh Cap-tain!

You, oh Cap-tain! You, oh Cap-tain Ses-a-maul!

(All)
A sneak-y, cun-ning, hand-some thief_Who leaves his vic-tims filled with grief.

(Capt. Sesamaul)
Who is the rich-est of them all?

(Robbers)
You, oh Cap-tain Ses-a-maul!

(All)
Gold and sil-ver, pearls and rub-ies, such wealth is found on-ly in the mo-vies.
Yo-ho! Yo-ho! Yo-ho, yo-ho, yo-ho!
We are men with hearts of stone. All who see us cry and groan.

(Sesamaul)
Who is the great-est of them all?

(Robbers)
You, oh Cap-tain! You, oh Cap-tain! You, oh Cap-tain Ses-a-maul!

CAPTAIN [*As he brandishes sword*]: Who is the bravest of them all?

THIEVES: You, oh Captain! You, oh Captain!
              You, oh Captain Ses-a-maul!

ALL: A sneaky, cunning, handsome thief,
              Who leaves his victims filled with grief.

CAPTAIN: Who is the richest of them all?

THIEVES: You, oh Captain Ses-a-maul!

ALL: Gold and silver, pearls and rubies,
              Such wealth is found only in the movies.
              Yo-ho! Yo-ho!
              Yo-ho, yo-ho, yo-ho!
              We are men with hearts of stone.
              All who see us cry and groan.

CAPTAIN: Who is the greatest of us all?

THIEVES: You, oh Captain! You, oh Captain!
              You, oh Captain Ses-a-maul!

CAPTAIN: Open Sesame! [*Clash of cymbals as curtain opens.* KASSIM *is hiding behind a bag of gold, but his cloak is still visible. Piled up in the middle of the floor is all of the treasure that* KASSIM *had planned to take with him.*] Woe to us! Our treasure cave has been discovered.

FIRST THIEF: It looks like someone was planning to carry off all of our treasure.

SECOND THIEF: Alas, someone must know our magic password.

THIRD THIEF: I have a feeling that the intruder is still here.

CAPTAIN: Search men, leave not a stone unturned. Guards, stay at the door. [KASSIM *runs to another hiding place closer to the door, near front of stage. The* GUARDS *see him and grab him.*]

CAPTAIN: Guards, hold fast. Make sure he does not escape.

KASSIM [*Kneels before* CAPTAIN]: Have mercy on me! I will go away and never tell anyone of your secret.

CAPTAIN: Guards, shut him up. Bring him into the back of the cave. We don't need him to give us advice. Men, gather round, we must discuss this serious problem. [*Men half kneel about him.*] This man must be killed.

JAMAL: Captain, he must have accomplices. How can we make sure that we discourage all who might have learned of our secret?

ABOU HASSAM: Captain Sesamaul, I have a suggestion.

CAPTAIN: It had better be good.

ABOU HASSAM: We must frighten his accomplices in such a manner that they will be too terrified to enter our cave again.

CAPTAIN: Splendid idea! Guards kill that man and cut his body into quarters. We shall hang the parts on the door of the cave so that no one else will dare to enter.

Curtain Closes

[*Spotlight is again thrown on corner where* SCHEHERAZADE *is telling her story to* SULTAN *and* LITTLE SISTER.]

SCHEHERAZADE: Alas, a bloody end came to poor Kassim! The four quarters of his body were hung over the entrance of the cave. When the thieves had finished and there was nothing more to detain them, they left the cave, planning to plunder more caravans. Meanwhile, Kassim's wife was very worried about the safety of her husband. Therefore, Ali Baba went to the cave to see what had happened to his brother. He was deeply grieved to discover how Kassim had met his death. But his sorrow did not prevent him from thinking quickly. He hastened to hide his brother's body on his donkey and hurried back to Kassim's house. Now, in the house of Kassim there was a slave girl named Morjeaneh. She was not only loyal and brave, but very wise as well. To Morjeaneh, Ali Baba went and told her the whole frightful story. [*Spotlight out.* ALI BABA *and* MORJEANEH *enter together in front of curtain.*]

Scene VI: Street Scene

ALI BABA: Now remember, Morjeaneh, you must try to keep your mistress quiet. It is most important that we make it look as though Kassim died a natural death. Otherwise, the robbers will kill us all.

MORJEANEH: I understand, good master, do not worry. [*Bows to him as he exits at right of curtain. As they were talking, a* COBBLER *had entered in front of the curtain from the left of the stage. He spreads out a small rug, then sits down, crosslegged, on it, takes out leather and awl and begins to work.* MORJEANEH *crosses in front of curtain to* COBBLER *and bows.*]

MORJEANEH: Peace be with you, Baba Mustapha. I hear you are the best leather worker of our city. The job I have in mind for you requires a good eye and a skillful hand. [*She places a gold coin in his palm.*]

BABA MUSTAPHA: You can see that I have a good eye, proved by the fact that I am already at work in this early morning dim light. You can see I have a steady hand by the samples of the work around me. You can find out if I have a stout heart by putting me to the test.

MORJEANEH: There will be another gold piece for you when you are finished. But, first, I must blindfold you. [*She ties a heavy silk scarf over his eyes and leads him back to the place where she had been talking to* ALI BABA *and takes him behind curtain.*]

[*Spotlight again on* SCHEHERAZADE *while she continues this part of her story.*]

SCHEHERAZADE: So it came to pass that Baba Mustapha, the leather maker, sewed up Kassim's body for a fine burial. When he was finished, Morjeaneh paid him, blindfolded him again and led him through the streets to his shop before the people of the town were up and about. When the funeral was held the next day, everyone believed that Kassim had just died of a sudden stroke. Since Kassim and his wife had no children, all his wealth went to Ali Baba, who moved into his brother's fine house. Kassim's widow became part of Ali Baba's household and the latter's son, Kerezan, took over his uncle's business. But there was trouble brewing for Ali Baba in the cave of the robbers. [*Spotlight off.*]

Scene VII: Robbers' Cave

The men are seated around their CAPTAIN *who is talking to them as the curtain rises on the dimly lit Robbers' Cave.*

CAPTAIN: As long as anyone besides us knows of this cave and the secret password, we are in danger. It is plain to see that someone knows how to enter our cave or the intruder's body we hung on the walls would still be here.

JAMAL: Brilliant deduction, Captain.

CAPTAIN: Now, one of the boldest and most skillful among you must go into town disguised as a traveling merchant. He must listen very carefully and try to hear any talk of the man we have killed. Any volunteers? Twenty pieces of gold to the man who succeeds.

[*There is no response. Some of the* THIEVES *shake their heads, others just look away.*]

CAPTAIN: A bag of gold to the man who can do this daring task successfully.

FIRST THIEF: That's a fortune!

SECOND THIEF: A bag of gold!

THIRD THIEF: What good is a bag of gold? If one of us is captured, we'll be killed for all the crimes we've committed.

ABOU HASSAM: I'll risk my life for a bag of gold! I'm on my way.

THIRD THIEF: Wish for luck, you'll need it.

CAPTAIN: Good luck, Abou Hassam. Our future depends on your success. [*Waves good-by, and fourth* ROBBER *exits.*] Well, he is on his way. But if Abou Hassam fails . . . [CAP-

TAIN *makes a gesture of cutting one's throat.*] *Death to the Intruders!*

Scene VIII: Street Scene

BABA MUSTAPHA *comes out from behind curtain and sets up shop and begins to work.*

ABOU HASSAM: There's a leather worker; he might be able to help me. Is it possible that you can see what you're doing in such dim light?

BABA MUSTAPHA: Even though I'm old, I have very good eyes. Why just yesterday I sewed together the body of a dead man in less light than I have now.

ABOU HASSAM [*Aside*]: This must be my lucky day. I do not want to learn your secret. The only thing I desire of you is to show me the house where you did your work.

BABA MUSTAPHA: Even if I were inclined to do you that favor, I assure you I cannot. I was taken to a certain place whence I was led blindfolded to the house. After my work was completed, I was blindfolded and brought back in the same manner.

ABOU HASSAM: Do you not have any idea of the direction you took?

BABA MUSTAPHA: Perhaps I will find my way there again.

ABOU HASSAM: Let me blindfold your eyes in the same place from where you were led to the house. I promise you two more gold pieces if you succeed in helping me locate the house.

BABA MUSTAPHA: I will try to remember. We walked over here and then I was blindfolded. [THIEF *puts his scarf over* BABA MUSTAPHA'S *eyes.*] We walked ahead and carefully avoided the puddle in the middle of the path. [THIEF *looks, can't see any puddle, so he lightly taps forehead, as if* BABA MUSTAPHA *is slightly "touched." Then he shrugs his shoulders, as if to indicate what has he to lose by following the* COBBLER.]

BABA MUSTAPHA: Then we turned ever so slightly in this direction until we arrived at this particular spot. [*Stops, thinks a moment, then slowly turns to the right, shakes his head and then points dramatically to the left.*] There should be a door with three steps right there!

ABOU HASSAM: There is! You have found the place. Here are the two pieces of gold I have promised you. But, before I take you back, I must mark this door with a chalk mark so that I can recognize it again. [*Takes out chalk and puts a big X on door. The painted doors are tacked to wall of auditorium, with steps leading up to them. They should be on the wall of the auditorium near the right side of the stage, but not too close to the platform on which the* SCHEHERAZADE *scenes are played. A spotlight can be used, when needed, to light this area.*]

ABOU HASSAM: Now, my friend, let me take you back to the street of shops where I found you. [*They walk back to* BABA MUSTAPHA's *stall.*] Good-by, my fine cobbler, you have done me a great service. [*Exits.*]

BABA MUSTAPHA: Well, it is still very early in the morning, but I have earned so much gold I will not bother to work any more today. I'll close my shop. [*Whistles as he picks up his tools and leather goods and rug and exits, humming.*]

MORJEANEH [*Offstage voice*]: I'm going to the market to get the food we need tonight for dinner. [*Enters at right, in front of curtain, starts to pass marked front door and then stops and takes a second look.*] What is this? I've never noticed such a strange chalk mark on the front door to my master's home before. Why should anyone mark just one door? That troubles me. I like it not. I have some chalk in my purse that I think I had better use to put a similar mark on all of the doors near my master's home. [*Does this and looks very pleased.*] And now all the doors look alike. [*She crosses in front of curtain and exits at left.*]

[*Lights dim.* CAPTAIN OF THIEVES *enters with* ABOU HASSAM.]

ABOU HASSAM: Then we walked down this narrow street and right at the end of this row of houses I put the chalk mark. See? [*Points to first door.*]

CAPTAIN: Fool! Why is there also a chalk mark here and here? How can we tell which one is the right door? You've been tricked! You shall be punished for bringing me into the city on a worthless trip! Let us get out of here before we are recognized and captured. [*Both quickly exit.*]

[*Spotlight on* SCHEHERAZADE *set.*]

SCHEHERAZADE: The Captain was very angry that one of his men had bungled the job. It was decided that this thief was deserving of death and he was beheaded. Another man volunteered to go for the two bags of gold. Baba Mustapha took him to the same place, but this time the thief made a mark in red chalk, which was hardly noticeable. Nothing, however, escaped the sharp eyes of Morjeaneh.

DUNYUZAD: I know what she must have done. She probably put red chalk marks on all the other doors, just like last time.

SCHEHERAZADE: That is just what she did. The Captain was so angry that he had this thief killed, too. Then he realized that he would have to do the investigation himself.

SULTAN: Ah, now the Captain of the robbers is showing his own bravery! There is an old Persian saying, "Never send a boy on a man's errand."

SCHEHERAZADE: That is very true, Sire, as the Captain had discovered. He, too, went to Baba Mustapha, but he made no chalk marks. Instead, he carefully memorized the location of the house. Then he went back to the hideout in the cave. [*Spotlight off.*]

Scene IX: Home of Ali Baba

Off stage voices and clatter of horses. CAPTAIN *and* JAMAL, *a thief, enter.*

CAPTAIN: Now remember, you and the men are to stay hidden in the jars, until I throw a handful of pebbles into the courtyard. At this signal, climb out at once and put to death everyone in Ali Baba's house. [*Crosses in front of curtain, goes over to doors on right. After examining all of the doorways carefully, he smiles smugly as he recognizes* ALI BABA'S *house and knocks on the door.*]

MORJEANEH [*Pulls aside curtain, pokes head out from right side of stage*]: What is your business with my master, Ali Baba?

CAPTAIN: Ah, beautiful maiden, it is most urgent that I speak to Ali Baba immediately.

MORJEANEH: Wait until I speak with him. What did you say your name was?

CAPTAIN: I am called . . . uh . . . Sabour, the oil merchant.

MORJEANEH: Wait.

[CAPTAIN *adjusts clothing so that knife is well hidden.* ALI BABA *enters in front of curtain on right side of stage.*]

ALI BABA: What is your business with me?

CAPTAIN: I have heard of your kindness and generosity from many of the merchants I deal with in this fair city. I have arrived late after traveling very far today and my donkeys are tired. If you will allow me to stay the night, I will pay you well. See, I have brought with me nineteen donkeys and each carries two great oil jars. [*Points toward left of stage.*]

ALI BABA: This is not an inn, my friend. But you are welcome to stay as my guest. Come into my home. One of my servants will feed the donkeys and bed them down for the night.

CAPTAIN: May Allah bless you. [ALI BABA *and* CAPTAIN *walk behind curtains on right as stage curtains open. The scene is the home of* ALI BABA. ALI BABA'S WIFE *and* KASSIM'S WIFE *are seated, talking to each other.* KEREZAN *is polishing a dagger.*]

ALI BABA [*Enters*]: My dears, I have a guest for the evening.

ALI BABA'S WIFE: We will retire to the women's quarters. [*They exit to left.*]

ALI BABA [*Calls to hallway*]: Won't you come in, Sabour. [SABOUR *enters.*] I would like you to meet my son, Kerezan. [KEREZAN *and* SABOUR *bow to each other.* ALI BABA *claps for* ZAIDEH *and gives him orders.*] Zaideh, my guest has many donkeys with oil jars in our courtyard. Bed down the animals and place the jars in a safe place from any robbers.

CAPTAIN: Uh . . . oh . . . uh . . . oh no . . . please don't bother. Leave them just as they are.

KEREZAN: Would you like to smoke a pipe?

[MORJEANEH *and* MIRYAN *set table and bring in food while the men smoke a water pipe.*]

ALI BABA: Do you not find it dangerous to travel so late at night? Are you not afraid of robbers?

CAPTAIN: I lead a very interesting life and meet many different people. I've even met thieves who, by the grace of Allah, robbed me not. This robber captain seemed to have a brilliant mind. I certainly enjoy my adventurous life.

ALI BABA: You may have your adventures. I prefer to be safe at home with my family. Won't you try our wine? It is especially good; Zaideh, pour the wine for our guest.

KEREZAN: We make our own wine from the grapes we buy in the market place.

CAPTAIN: Thank you, I would enjoy a glass of wine. [*They continue to talk in low voices as* MORJEANEH *and her assistant,* MIRYAN, *walk to front of stage.*]

MORJEANEH [*Speaking in a low voice to servant*]: We have not enough oil for the evening meal. I will refill it from one of the many jars of oil the merchant has brought to our courtyard. He will never miss a little oil. You may start serving the soup and bread. It will take me just a moment.

[MORJEANEH *exits as* MIRYAN *brings over serving tables and serves.* MORJEANEH *enters, looking flustered, puts oil on table, calls* MIRYAN *aside.*]

MORJEANEH [*Whispers*]: You attend to all of the meal, Miryan. There is some important work I must do right away. Keep the fire hot in our stove. [*Curtain closes.*]

[*Spotlight on* SCHEHERAZADE *set.*]

SCHEHERAZADE: Morjeaneh was very frightened when she discovered robbers in the oil jars. She had moved so quietly the thieves didn't realize they had been noticed.

[*During this short scene,* MORJEANEH *enters from right, in front of curtain, walking slowly, for the gold pitcher she is carrying is filled with hot oil. She crosses in front of curtain, then exits on the left side. She quickly reappears and, holding the empty pitcher, casually rushes back to other side of curtain, where she again disappears. She enters once more, carrying her pitcher slowly, for it is again filled with hot oil, crosses stage in front of curtain and exits on left. This action is repeated just three times while* SCHEHERAZADE *continues with her story.*]

SULTAN: Why did she do that?

SCHEHERAZADE: Well, quickly, before the robbers knew what was happening, Morjeaneh had drowned each one of them in hot oil.

SULTAN: But their Captain is still inside the house!

DUNYUZAD: Did the Captain kill Ali Baba?

SCHEHERAZADE: Morjeaneh was making plans on how to save her master as she walked back into the house.

[*Spotlight out.*]

Scene X: Later, in the Home of Ali Baba

ALI BABA'S *home. Men have finished dinner,* MIRYAN *is clearing off the table and the men are smoking water pipes.*

CAPTAIN: That was a delicious dinner. Your servants are

fine cooks.

ALI BABA: Morjeaneh is the finest. She takes care of everything. She also dances beautifully, which my son and I particularly enjoy. Would you like to see her dance?

CAPTAIN: I would, indeed.

ALI BABA: Kerezan, find Morjeaneh! Ask her to help entertain us with a dance. [MORJEANEH *enters.*]

KEREZAN: Here's Morjeaneh now. [*Gets up and walks over to her.*] Morjeaneh, Father would like you to do a dance in honor of our guest.

MORJEANEH: I will try to do my best to please you. Kerezan, I will need more room. Would you be so kind as to help me move this table? [KEREZAN *helps her and they move table near front of stage.*]

MORJEANEH [*Whispers*]: Kerezan, do not turn around or show surprise. I have discovered that Sabour is really the Captain of the thieves. He is here to kill all of us. I am sure he has a dagger under his sash. You show him your unusual collection of daggers while I get ready.

KEREZAN: Why can't I just get a dagger and save us now?

MORJEANEH: It's too dangerous. Wait until I give you a signal by throwing my red scarf, then, you surprise him! [*Turns to* ALI BABA.] I will get my music, Master, and return quickly. [*Exits.*]

KEREZAN: Perhaps, sir, you would like to see an unusual collection of daggers that I own, while we are waiting for Morjeaneh?

CAPTAIN: Daggers? That would interest me. [*Quickly adds*] Even though I am a peace loving man. [KEREZAN *exits.*]

ALI BABA: My son has bought many beautiful jeweled swords and daggers in the market bazaars. He is very proud of the magnificent jewels on the handles and the fine metal work. [MORJEANEH *and* KEREZAN *enter together.*]

KEREZAN: Morjeaneh is ready to dance. I will show these

to you later.

[MORJEANEH *clashes on her tambourine and starts her dance, which begins as a quiet, lovely one but gradually gets more and more wild. Suddenly, she whirls about, tossing her scarfs around, and finally throws a bright red one at the* CAPTAIN. *At this sign,* KEREZAN *jumps and swings a dagger at the* CAP-TAIN, *who, realizing he has been discovered, pulls out his own dagger and defends himself. They continue to fight off stage.* ALI BABA, *all confused, can't understand what is happening and rushes over to the doorway and gasps as* CAPTAIN *gives a loud groan.* MORJEANEH *watches intently.* ALI BABA *and* KEREZAN *re-enter.*]

KEREZAN: Morjeaneh, you saved our lives! The Captain of the thieves is dead. He tripped on the stairs, fell on his own dagger and died instantly.

ALI BABA: My dear Morjeaneh, you have saved the lives of all my family. I wish to reward you and give you your freedom. You no longer have to work for me, but I do not know how we will get along without you. Is there anything else I can do to show you how thankful I am?

KEREZAN: May I ask something of you, Father? For many months Morjeaneh and I have known we love each other. Will you give us your permission to marry?

ALI BABA *nods and* KEREZAN *takes* MORJEANEH *by the hand. They look at each other with devotion, as the curtain falls.*]

Epilogue

MEELING *and* TEELING *each enter from side of stage, meet in center, bow to each other, then to audience.*

MEELING: And so, in time, the wedding was held.

TEELING: There was feasting and merrymaking.

MEELING: Then for years and years—

TEELING: Whenever anyone in Ali Baba's family wanted some of the world's riches—

MEELING: He had only to go to a certain rock and call out:

BOTH IN UNISON: OPEN SESAME!

[*Clash of cymbals.*]

[*Bow to audience, then to each other and then both exit.*]

PRODUCTION NOTES

This play should obviously be given a Persian setting. The over-all effect should be Oriental, rich and colorful. Consult pictures in the various colorful editions of the story for suggestions on costumes, scenery, properties and lighting.

Dick Whittington

BY MARY REA LEWIS

AND HER FIFTH GRADE AT HORACE MANN–LINCOLN SCHOOL,

TEACHERS COLLEGE, COLUMBIA UNIVERSITY

Characters

DICK WHITTINGTON
APPLE-MAN
WAGONER
MAN
COOK
MR. FITZWARREN
ALICIA
CAPTAIN KENT
FIRST MAID
SECOND MAID
KING
QUEEN
SERVANT
JOHN

DICK WHITTINGTON

Dick Whittington lived during the last part of the thirteenth and the first part of the fourteenth century. The story of his early years is lost in legend. But we do know that he lived and died and lies buried near the Tower of London; that he was four times Lord Mayor of London; was knighted by King Henry V and was a very, very rich man, leaving a vast fortune to charities.

The story of Dick Whittington and his cat has always been a great favorite with children . . . the eternal success story of the poor boy who reached the top through his own goodness and efforts.

Act I

On the road to London—a clearing in the woods. Enter DICK, *discouraged and tired.*

DICK [*Seeing a log on the road side*]: At last! A place to rest. [*Sits down wearily, rubs feet and ankles.*] I must have traveled more than twenty miles today. My feet ache so. I wish there was a stream nearby; cold water would make them feel better. [*Pushes hair back from face.*] It wouldn't do any harm to my face, either. I'll rest here for a moment before I go further. It will soon be nightfall and I want to be out of the woods before darkness comes. [*Looks in knapsack for food.*] Not even a crumb left! Oh, I'm so hungry. I don't know whether I can go on any further—it's such a long journey. I've wondered often this day why I ever ventured away from my own village. Of course, there is no reason why I should have stayed there. For weeks I've tried to find a means to earn my way. I've begged on the streets and along the water front, but I got so few coins. Everyone was as poor as I—no one could spare even a ha'penny for a homeless boy. I shiver now when I think of those cold wintry nights that I spent sleeping in doorways. Whenever I passed houses that were lighted and warm, I'd just stand and stare and stare at them. Once an officer was going to put me in prison for peeping into the windows of a grand house. It was such a lovely house—I couldn't go past it. When the officer seized me, I let out a cry. I was so frightened. An old gentleman heard me and before the officer could hurry me away, he came over to us. "What's the trouble, officer?" he asked. "Just another thieving waif," he replied. "No, no!" I cried, "I'm not a thief. I may be dirty and ragged; I may have no home, or I may be terribly, terribly hungry; but I never steal." That old gentleman believed me, for he got me free from the officer. Then he gave me two shillings and told me to go on my way. That night I bought a sugared bun—and oh, it was so good! Ever since that night I've wanted to be a grand gentleman so that I could help other people. That's why I'm going to London Town now. I know there's a chance there for me— if—ever I get there. [*Looks around*]. I wonder how much farther it is. If I follow this road—is it the shortest way? [*Gets up and looks off stage.*] There are wheel marks going on and on down the road. It must lead to the city. [*As* DICK *talks, an* APPLE-MAN *approaches from the opposite side.*]

APPLE-MAN: What ho, my lad! Are you lost?

DICK: Oh, sir, you frightened me! No, I don't think I'm lost. I'm on my way to London Town. This is the road, isn't it?

APPLE-MAN: Yea, and that it is. If you follow it to the edge of the clearing, you'll come right to the high road. Follow that and soon you'll be in London Town.

DICK: Is it far, sir?

APPLE-MAN: I hear it is. I've never been there, but friends of mine were there once. It's a grand city, I hear, [*Confidentially.*] And do you know, lad, I'm told that it's the richest place in the world. It is rumored that even the streets are paved with gold.

DICK: Gold? Oh, sir, surely not in the streets!

APPLE-MAN: That's what I hear; mind you, though I've never seen it—just heard about it.

DICK [*Starts off, turns to* APPLE-MAN]: Thank you, sir, for telling me this. I'll come back some day with some of the gold and share it with you.

APPLE-MAN: I'll be waiting—if you're not too long in getting back. [DICK *starts off again.*] Lad! [DICK *turns back.*] You've got a kind heart and a noble spirit; but I think 'twill need more to make a grand gentleman of you.

DICK: What do you mean, sir?

APPLE-MAN: You look so worn and hungry now that I doubt you'll ever get to London. It's a long trip, you know. When did you eat last?

DICK [*Hesitating*]: Oh—not long ago.

APPLE-MAN: Not long ago! That could be an hour—or—maybe a day ago! And what did you eat? [DICK *hangs head.*] I thought so! [*Reaches into bag.*] I haven't much left from the day at the market, but here! I'll share with you! A half loaf from my lunch—and—two nice red apples!

DICK: Oh, sir, I couldn't take them! [*Looks at them longingly.*]

APPLE-MAN: No? Well, I'll bargain with you. You take the food and when you're a rich and grand gentleman, you can pay me for them. You'll come back dressed in fine cloth and lace—drawn in a magnificent coach, and stop at the square to ask the whereabouts of Jack, the apple-man. And I'll step forward and say, unconscious-like, "Oh, my young friend, Lord—" But who'll you be?

DICK: Not a lord, friend; just plain Dick Whittington.

APPLE-MAN: Nay, not plain Dick Whittington—*Lord* Dick Whittington! [*Bows low.*]

DICK: You jest with me! [*Looks at food.*] It's a bargain, sir. I'll take your food in exchange for my promise to pay you many times over when I make my fortune. [*Both laugh heartily. Unseen approaches the* WAGONER.]

WAGONER: Fortune must have smiled on you this day, Jack, the apple-man. [DICK *and* APPLE-MAN *turn, astonished.*]

APPLE-MAN: Oh, my friend, 'tis indeed true. Fortune in the form of Lord Whittington. [*Bows low.*]

[WAGONER *glances critically at* DICK.]

WAGONER: This stripling—*this* is Lord Whittington?

APPLE-MAN: No other, my friend. He's on his way to London Town to claim his fortune.

WAGONER: And your coach, my Lord—does it wait on the high road?

DICK: Nay, sir. I have neither coach nor steed—nor am I a nobleman. Just Dick Whittington, homeless, penniless—a wayfarer on his way to London Town.

WAGONER: You've heard the tale of gold, then—how 'tis so plentiful that it's used to pave the streets. Even the wayfarer can fill his purse as he goes about the city.

DICK: The apple-man has just told me about it; but I know that such a report lacks truth. If 'twere true, then all the world would go to London, and there would be too little left for another fortune.

WAGONER: 'Tis the way I'm thinking, too, lad. But if it's not a fortune you seek, why go you there?

DICK: 'Tis a fortune I seek, sir, but not by picking it from the streets. I seek work and a chance to grow into useful manhood.

WAGONER: I hear that London's a busy mart; many may find work there. But you—why you're but a lad. What can you do?

DICK: Many tasks, sir, if I have the opportunity to prove myself. That is all I ask. But I must be on my way now. [*Turns to* APPLE-MAN.] Many thanks, sir, to you. I shall not forget our bargain. [*To* WAGONER.] Could you direct me, sir, to the shortest way?

WAGONER: Follow this road to the edge of the clearing— that's the high road ahead. Follow it. London's at the end.

DICK: Thank you, sir. [*Starts off, stops and turns to the two men talking together.*] And the distance, sir? Is it less than one day's journey?

WAGONER: Not unless you have wings. I'd say that, if you walk fast and waste no time along the wayside, you'd be in London Town by tomorrow night. [*Continues conversation with* APPLE-MAN.]

DICK [*Disappointed*]: Tomorrow night! [*Stops thoughtfully.*] 'Tis much further than I thought. I'm already exhausted— [*Looks in knapsack.*] and I have but little food— [*Stops.*] I can't go on. I'll return! I'll find some way— [*In whisper.*] There are those bells again—what are they saying? Listen! [*Slowly.*] "Turn again, Dick Whittington, thrice Lord Mayor of London!" What do they mean? Why do they echo *my* name? [*Turns again to* WAGONER *and* APPLE-MAN.] Pardon, sirs, those bells, sirs, what do they say?

APPLE-MAN [*Listening*]: Night—again;—night's come again—night—again—all's well!

WAGONER: Aye, right again. I must be on my way. Good night, my friend. My horse has had a long rest this afternoon —he'll think I've deserted him. [*Starts off.*] Good night! [*Turns to* DICK.] If you're leaving now, lad, I could take you to the high road in my wagon.

DICK: Oh, thank you, sir. That I should appreciate so much.

WAGONER: Well, come then, with me. It's no royal coach I have—just a small wagon.

DICK: Thank you, sir. [WAGONER *and* DICK *start off.* DICK *turns to* APPLE-MAN.] Lose not patience, my benefactor, I

shall not forget you nor your kindness.
[*Exit.*]

APPLE-MAN: Good fortune to you, lad. You're a brave boy and true.

Act II
Scene I: *A Street in London*

DICK *enters slowly—picks up pebble from street.*

DICK: Not gold! Just a pebble. I've traveled along many streets this day but no gold anywhere. [*Sits on a doorstep and takes a piece of bun from his knapsack. Munches on it. A man passes and almost falls, as he stumbles over* DICK's *feet.*]

MAN: What means this? Who are you? What do you mean by taking possession of Mr. Fitzwarren's doorway? Why did you try to throw me?
[DICK *jumps to his feet.*]

DICK: Your pardon, sir, I did not mean—

MAN [*Angrily*]: Then what did you mean?

DICK: I just sat here a moment to rest, sir. I'm very tired. For three days I haven't had much rest.

MAN: And why not? [*Looks critically at* DICK.] You haven't seen much water, either. I've never seen a dirtier little rogue. Go home at once, or . . .

DICK: I have no home, sir.

MAN: Well, get on your way, then, before Fitzwarren's cook sees you. [DICK *starts off dejectedly. Meets the* COOK. *Holds out his ragged cap.*]

DICK: A penny, mistress, if it please you.

COOK: Please me! Indeed it does not please me, you impudent little beggar. I work hard for my money and I have no intention of parting with it at every beggar's cry. Away now, before I thrash you.

DICK: But, mistress, I'm so hungry I can't go any further. If I had a penny, I could buy some food. Then I wouldn't bother you.

COOK: There's nothing but beggars in this town. Every time I go on the street some lazy urchin thrusts his cap at me crying, "A penny, mistress, only a penny!" Why don't they work as honest people do?

DICK: I'd gladly work for you if you'd let me.

COOK: I wouldn't allow such filth in my kitchen! Take yourself off at once before you spoil the doorstep.

[*Enter* MR. FITZWARREN *and* ALICIA.]

MR. FITZ: What have we here, Cook?

COOK: Another lazy beggar, sir. I found him causing a disturbance on your doorstep.

DICK: Sir, I meant no harm. I was walking along—oh, so tired—I couldn't walk any further. Your doorstep looked so inviting. I—just—sat—down.

ALICIA: Father, I believe the lad is hungry.

MR. FITZ: Nonsense, Alicia, I believe he's a worthless little beggar, just as Cook says.

ALICIA [*Sitting beside* DICK]: What's your name?

DICK [*Trying to rise*]: Dick, mistress, Dick Whittington.

ALICIA: Where's your home, Dick?

DICK: I have no home.

ALICIA: Then where do you live?

DICK: Any place I can find shelter.

MR. FITZ: You see, Alicia, it's just as I said. He's a worthless little beggar, playing on your sympathy.

ALICIA: No, Father, I do not believe that. [*To* DICK.] Why do you not work, Dick? You look old enough to work.

DICK: That I would gladly do, mistress, but no one will have me. I've tried and tried—oh, so many times, to do anything to earn a penny. Everyone pushes me aside. I've tried to beg occasionally, but in three days all I've received is a ha'penny.

ALICIA: Poor lad! [*Looks in purse hanging on belt.*] Here, Dick, is a coin.

DICK: Thank you for your kindness, mistress, but I could not take it from you. 'Tis all you have.

ALICIA [*To her* FATHER]: Father, can't *you* help Dick in some way?

MR. FITZ: Perhaps, Alicia, perhaps. [*To* COOK.] Cook, aren't there some odd jobs about the house that this lad could do?

COOK: We-eell!

MR. FITZ: See to it that he goes to work at once. [*To* DICK.] Do whatever she bids, lad.

ALICIA: But, Father, he's hungry.

MR. FITZ: Cook, first take this lad to the kitchen and give him a good dinner. Set him some tasks to do—running errands, fetching wood, drawing water—you know best how he can help you.

DICK: Oh, thank you, sir. I'll work hard, sir. I'll do my best.

MR. FITZ: I know you will. Do whatever Cook asks and I'm certain you will succeed.

DICK [*To* ALICIA]: Thank you, Mistress Fitzwarren, for interceding for me.

ALICIA [*Smiling*]: You deserve help, I think. [*To* FATHER.] Thank you, Father.

MR. FITZ: And Dick—

DICK: Sir?

MR. FITZ: There's an empty room in the garret. You shall sleep there.

DICK: Oh, sir, you are so kind—I'm so excited that I've forgotten my hunger.

MR. FITZ: Cook will soon attend to that. Come, Alicia, we must continue on your way. Cook, attend to the lad's needs at once.

[*Exeunt* ALICIA *and* MR. FITZWARREN.]

COOK [*Gingerly holding* DICK's *shoulder*]: So you want to

work hard? Well, I'll see to it that you *do*. Come along, now.
[*Exit.*]

Act II
Scene II

[*In the kitchen.* COOK *is busy.* DICK *cleans floor.*]

COOK: Hurry, you rascal. All day you've dawdled over your work. [DICK *yawns.*] That's right! Yawn in my face! Rudeness —base rudeness is what I call that! [*Rushes toward* DICK, *who begins to scrub furiously.*]

DICK: But, Cook, I've done all my work except this corner of the kitchen, and it'll be finished before you finish the pudding.

COOK: Finished your work! [*Inspects kitchen.*] Why, it's only half done. What about the scullery?

DICK: I cleaned every inch of it.

COOK: Humpf! And the pans—I suppose they're all scoured?

DICK: Pans scoured and kettles polished until you can see yourself in them!

COOK: Be nimble then, and in a hurry, too, for I want you to fetch more wood for the fires.

DICK [*Muttering to himself*]: Nimble! Fetch! Carry! That's all she knows.

COOK: And what are you grumbling about now? I'll teach you respect. [*Starts after* DICK *with a broom.*] The master told me to take care of you and I intend to do it.

DICK [*Pleading*]: Please, Cook—

COOK: And what do you think the master will say?—
[*Enter* ALICIA.]

ALICIA [*To* COOK]: I think he'll say that Dick does his work very well. Why are you so unkind to him?

COOK: Unkind? Why, Mistress Alicia, if you but knew how

I have to drive him to finish his work!

ALICIA: With a broom? Here, give that to me. [*Takes broom.*] I don't think my father would approve of your abuse of Dick. He's always busy. And you heard Father say only yesterday that he never has to tell Dick a second time to do anything. He's learning very quickly.

DICK: I try so hard to please the master—and you, too, Mistress Alicia.

ALICIA [*To* DICK]: We are both pleased with your work. Father told me to ask you about your room in the garret. Do the mice still bother you?

DICK: Oh, no, mistress, not since—

COOK: Not since you brought that cat here, I suppose. I'm telling you for the last time that you must get rid of it. Dirty thing! [*To* ALICIA.] Would you believe, mistress, that this thankless creature carries all the food from the kitchen to the garret to feed that prowling beast? What will the master say?

ALICIA: Enough of your scolding, Cook. Dick will not get rid of his cat, and that's my order. Do you understand?

DICK: She's a great comfort to me, mistress. She never prowls about, even though Cook says she does. All day she sleeps on the window ledge and never, never leaves the garret. As for food—I only take her scraps from my own dinner.

COOK: It would be better for you if you ate your food yourself, then you wouldn't be so tired all the time.

DICK: It's not food that I need to make me less tired. Before Puss came I never could sleep at night because the mice in the garret kept me awake. Since I've had her, she keeps the mice away and I'm beginning to sleep again. Soon she'll have killed them all and I'll get the rest I need.

ALICIA: I'm glad that you have her, Dick. She's yours and no one will take her from you. Don't worry any more about Cook's threats.

DICK: Thank you, mistress.

[*Exit* ALICIA.]

COOK: Aren't you the fine gentleman, sniffling and crying to Mistress Alicia. Do you suppose she could ever admire such a weakling? And mind you! Even though she threatens me, I'm warning you that that cat must not—it will not keep you from doing your full share of work so long as I am Cook in this household. [*Pauses.*] I'm going to the garden now to find John. When I get back, I shall expect to find this kitchen in perfect order.

[*Exit* COOK.]

DICK: Crosspatch! If it weren't for you, I'd be so happy here. [*Finishes scrubbing.*] There, that's finished! [*Takes pail.*] There's only one thing left to do. I must fill the log baskets so that, if it turns cold, Master can have a fire in the room. Then to the garret to tell Puss that she has a real home here with me and that no one will ever, ever, chase her away.

[*Exit.*]

Act II
Scene III: *Mr. Fitzwarren's Office*

MR. FITZ: And now, Daughter, I believe we have everything in readiness to conclude the business of preparing for the voyage of the *Unicorn*. Captain Kent and I have planned the trip carefully and our trading-ship is ready to sail tomorrow. [*To* CAPTAIN KENT.] You know, sir, it is my custom to allow each person in my household to contribute a share to our cargo. We entrust it to you to barter with the natives of far-away countries, hoping that, as heretofore, you will bring back to each one a generous profit from his undertaking.

CAPTAIN: That's noble of you, sir. If all goes well on this voyage, I believe that I can and will bargain well with the natives. As you know, they lack many of the goods which we have in great quantity here in England. Often their rulers are attracted by some unusual article, and, from their great fortunes, these rulers often pay fabulous sums, either in money or goods, just to own what we consider a commonplace article. If your household can profit from such deals, it is my honor to act for them as I would for you, sir, in large matters.

ALICIA [*To* CAPTAIN]: What is your first port of call, Captain?

CAPTAIN: I hope to sail directly for the rich coast of Barbary.

ALICIA: Isn't that a barbarous country, sir?

MR. FITZ: Enough of this questioning, Alicia. Call the servants—they must be ready by this time.

[*Exit* ALICIA—*enters almost immediately, followed by* SERVANTS. MR. F. *and* CAPTAIN K. *engage in quiet conversation.*]

MR. FITZ [*To* SERVANTS]: As you know, Captain Kent sails tomorrow with a cargo of my goods to trade with peoples in faraway countries. Each of you may have among your treasures some things which you also may wish to entrust to him. You may contribute from your savings, if you prefer, and Captain Kent will do his best for you on this trip.

MAN: Here, Captain Kent, is part of my profit from your last trip. [*Gives purse to* CAPTAIN.]

CAPTAIN: If all goes well on this trip, my man, you will double this amount.

1st MAID: Here, sir, is a lovely linen cloth which my grandmother wove for me several years ago. I stitched it myself during the past years.

MR. FITZ: That is a treasure, my girl, which may attract the eye of some fair maid. If she is as good a housekeeper as you, she will reward you for your work. [MAID *curtseys.*]

2nd MAID: I have here, sir, a pitcher which I bought last year at the fair. I should like you to take it with you.

ALICIA: If fortune favors you, Jane, you may buy more than one pitcher at next year's fair.

2nd MAID: I trust so, Mistress. [*Curtseys.*]

MR. FITZ: Now, Cook, what will your share be?

COOK: Well, sir— [*Hesitates.*]

ALICIA: Some grand surprise, I'll venture!

COOK: I haven't much, sir, for I've not been able to save much from my earnings.

MR. FITZ: Surely, Cook, you do not wish the *Unicorn* to sail without a contribution from you.

COOK: Would the lovely green feather from my last year's bonnet be worthy, sir?

CAPTAIN: A colored feather once brought a rich prize to its owner. A chief's wife saw it among our goods and would have nothing else. The chief gave me a packet of stones in exchange for it. Those stones turned out to be jewels. Thus the owner of the feather received a generous fortune and was able to buy a feather for every bonnet she wore.

ALICIA: Hurry and get it, Cook. We'll all be hoping that you will have equal good fortune.

COOK: I'll wrap it carefully and give it to the Captain's man.

MR. FITZ: That accounts for all of you, does it not? [*Looks over goods.*]

ALICIA: Oh, Father, you've forgotten Dick.

MR. FITZ: That I have—sorry, my lad, but I did not see you. Were you hiding?

DICK: No, sir, but I haven't a thing in the world to contribute. You know I possess nothing of my own. I wish I had just one small coin to contribute, sir. I'd gladly give it, with no thought of profit, just in gratitude for all the happiness you've brought me.

ALICIA: But Dick, you *do* have something.

DICK [*Puzzled*]: What, mistress?

ALICIA: Puss!

DICK: Oh, I couldn't let *her* go, mistress. Besides, who would want to buy a cat?

CAPTAIN: That is the chance you take, lad. If you send her with me, I shall try to get a fair price for her. If I am not successful, I shall bring her back to you. Besides, we can always use a cat on the ship.

MR. FITZ: Fetch your cat, Dick. I think she will bring good fortune to all of us.

DICK: Really, sir? Gladly then will I part with her.
[*Exit* DICK.]

COOK: Think you, Captain, that you will return within the year?

CAPTAIN: If we have fair winds, I believe we will make the trip in that time. We're undertaking a long and perilous voyage; but if we have patience and exercise skill, I hope for a safe and successful trip.

MAN: What route will you follow, sir?

CAPTAIN: We will sail down the Spanish coast, through the gates of Hercules and thence into the stormy Mediterranean. Eventually, we will reach the coast of Barbary, where we will barter our goods and gold in native markets and in the courts of native rulers.

ALICIA: I have heard that that country is wealthy and prosperous.

CAPTAIN: True, Mistress, and only too eager to secure our goods.
[*Enter* DICK *with cat.*]

DICK: Here, Captain, is my only treasure. I love her dearly and I shall be very lonely without her. [*Pats cat.*] Oh, Puss, what shall I do without you? I don't want to let you go.

ALICIA: Perhaps, Dick, we may be able to secure another cat for you to take Puss's place.

DICK: But another cat wouldn't be Puss. [*Pauses and then relinquishes cat.*] Be kind to her, sir, please. [*Wipes away tears.*]

CAPTAIN: You may be assured that I will. [DICK *rushes out.*]

MR. FITZ: That concludes our business; I believe you may now return to your duties. [*Exeunt* SERVANTS.] Come with me, Alicia, while we accompany the Captain to the door. A final wish of success for the voyage from you will speed him happily on his way.

[*Exeunt* ALICIA, MR. FITZWARREN, CAPTAIN KENT *and* SAILORS.]

Act III
Scene I: *Interior of Palace of King of Barbary*

KING [*To* SERVANT]: It is our understanding that the English trading ship has already anchored in our waters. Soon the Captain will come to our court to show his wares. As soon as he arrives, bring him to us at once, for we are eager to examine his cargo. Likewise, it is our wish to talk with the seamen about the long voyage they have undertaken, for we would learn from them the customs and ways of those who live in far-away lands.

QUEEN [*To* KING]: But first, Your Majesty, let us examine their goods. Always they bring such unusual merchandise, such wares of exquisite beauty.

SERVANT: Already the brave Captain and his men have arrived, Your Majesty. Even now they unpack their wares in the courtyard.

KING: Bring them to us at once.

[*Exit* SERVANT.]

KING [*To* QUEEN]: I trust that these traders have stopped at no other ports before they reached our shores. Our enemy tribesmen along the coast may have selected the best of their cargo and there will be little of value left for us.

QUEEN: We shall soon know when they show us their goods. If there be little of value, then we may know that we have little chance of trading further with our own subjects. But, let us not be too concerned, for I hear the approach of our guests.

[*Enter* SERVANT, *followed by* CAPTAIN KENT *and* SAILORS.]

KING [*To* CAPTAIN]: Welcome to our court; very seldom are we so honored by the presence of such brave seamen. We trust that your voyage was pleasant.

CAPTAIN: Your hospitality is a source of great satisfaction to us, Your Majesty. Our voyage was long and perilous; many times did we fear that we would have to seek shelter in some unknown land. Our skilled seamen, however, held to the course of your hospitable shore.

QUEEN: How long were you at sea?

CAPTAIN: It is many months since we left England. In that time we have not touched land until we arrived at your shores. [QUEEN *looks knowingly at* KING.]

KING: We trust that you have brought with you such wares and merchandise as we may trade successfully with you.

CAPTAIN: Our cargo is assembled in the courtyard. You will find quantities of grain from the fields of far-away England, bags of wool for your robes, rolls of cloth already woven, a variety of seeds which will grow plenteously in your fields, and works from the hands of our best artisans.

KING: That is well. [*To* SERVANT.] Command the Royal Treasurer to view these wares at once. If they meet with his pleasure, we shall require all of the cargo. Command him to send payment for the English goods which he selects.
[*Exit* SERVANT.]

CAPTAIN: Your Majesty's generosity is unequaled. In return for your trust, we bring to you and to your gracious Queen gifts from our master merchant in London.
[*Hands gift to* KING.]

KING: A rare and splendid gift. Carry to your master my expression of gratitude.
[CAPTAIN *hands gift to* QUEEN.]

QUEEN: So exquisite a gift requires more than words of gratitude. Carry to your master this packet of jewels in return for his great kindness.
[CAPTAIN *bows.*]

CAPTAIN: As is our custom, we brought lesser goods from the household of our master, trusting that we may barter with you and your court for such goods as are too little known in our own land.

KING: Display these wares for our consideration. [SEAMEN *bring goods.* KING *and* QUEEN *examine them carefully.*]

KING [*To* QUEEN]: Do they please your taste?

QUEEN: They are most beautiful. Gladly shall I exchange from my own treasures a payment for all of these. The artisans of our court cannot produce the like.

[*Enter* SERVANT, *who speaks quietly to* KING.]

KING: 'Tis well, then, Captain, we shall require all of your cargo. Tomorrow, our slaves shall carry to your ship quantities of copper and beaten brass and fifty of our finest rugs. The remainder of the price will be made in gold. And, now, it is our pleasure to extend the hospitality of our court to you so long as you remain guests in our land. We have prepared for your pleasure a royal feast—

[*Off-stage cries of fright. "The mice! The mice!"* QUEEN *excitedly rises and claps her hands—a* SERVANT *enters and drops on her knees at feet of* QUEEN.]

SERVANT: Your Majesty—Your *gracious* Majesty!

QUEEN: What means this confusion?

SERVANT: The mice, Your Majesty—they have come again.

KING: Pray, sir, pardon this discourtesy.

QUEEN: We are disgraced in the presence of our guests!

KING: These offensive creatures overrun the palace and bring great misfortune to our court.

CAPTAIN: That is indeed unfortunate.

KING: I would gladly give half of my treasure to be rid of them. But what can I do? The insect men of our kingdom cannot help us.

QUEEN: We are constantly plagued with them. At night, the royal chambers must be guarded to keep out these invaders.

CAPTAIN: Can you not kill them?

KING: But how?

CAPTAIN: I have on my ship a creature that will kill them. [CAPTAIN *murmurs to a* SAILOR, *who leaves stage.*]

KING: You have? Then pray bring it to us at once. If it has such magical power, gladly will I give you twice its weight in gold in exchange for it.

QUEEN: And I will add equal weight in jewels. No matter how fierce it is, it will be the most honored member of our court.

CAPTAIN: This creature will soon drive the mice away. The mere scent of it will frighten them into the sea, for it is the sworn enemy of all mice.

[*Enter* SAILOR *with Puss.*]

CAPTAIN: Here, Your Majesty, is Puss.

KING: Puss? Never have I known or heard about such a creature.

CAPTAIN: Puss is her name. She is a cat.

QUEEN: So small a creature!

CAPTAIN: Small, indeed, but a mighty hunter of the pest which disturbs your palace.

KING: I must have this cat. [*Claps hands at* SERVANT.] Bring my chest of gold and the Queen's jewel chest at once.

QUEEN: Is she fierce?

CAPTAIN: Nay, Your Majesty, she is gentle and kind to humans. [*Puts cat in* QUEEN's *lap.*] Stroke her fur.

QUEEN: Oh, she is so soft and warm.

[*Enter* SERVANT *with chest.*]

KING: Here, Captain, is the price we promised you.

CAPTAIN: I dislike to part with her, Your Majesty, but I know your need is great, so I am happy to give her to you. Send her at once to your kitchen. Ere morning comes, you shall be rid of the mice.

KING: Such a happy occasion demands more ceremony. We shall escort our Queen herself to the kitchen and there release the cat for her noble work.

[SERVANTS *carry chests as they lead procession.*]

Act III
Scene II: *Six months later*

ALICIA [*Rushing in*]: Father, John has just reported that Captain Kent and his men are coming now.

MR. FITZ: Then, my child, tell the servants to be ready when I call for them.

ALICIA: No need for that, Father, they've been waiting and ready all morning. John has told them the news by this time. If you were to go to the kitchen, you'd find them all waiting nervously to hear the glad tidings he has for them.

[*Knock at door.*]

MR. FITZ: Enter!

[*Enter* CAPTAIN *and* SAILORS—CAPTAIN *shakes hands with* MR. FITZWARREN *and bows to* ALICIA.]

Welcome, Welcome, Captain Kent! We are doubly glad to see you, for disturbing rumors about your safety had reached our ears.

CAPTAIN: For that reason, I hastened here as fast as I could. I, too, heard some of these tales when we anchored. We had a most dangerous return voyage; but never did we lose confidence that we would weather all perils and return to our home land.

ALICIA: How long did the voyage require, sir?

CAPTAIN: We should have made it in four months. Instead, we have sailed six months since we left the Barbary coast.

MR. FITZ: What extended the time, Captain?

CAPTAIN: Contrary winds and rough seas caused most of our troubles. We had to alter our course several times, to escape the pirates who were driving all trading ships into their own secret ports. We carried such valuable cargo that I feared we should be attacked by them. Fortunately, we were able to elude them.

ALICIA: How exciting, Captain! Do tell us more about the pirates.

MR. FITZ: Later, my child. The Captain has other and more

important matters to attend to first. [*To* CAPTAIN.] Tell me, sir, how did you fare with the trading?

CAPTAIN: Most prosperously, sir. Barbary was our only port of call, for the King of that rich country bought our entire cargo. He was most generous to us, too. The goods which we obtained through barter are still aboard the *Unicorn* and will be unloaded at your orders. Here, sir, is the gold in payment for the goods we sold. [*Presents bag.*]

MR. FITZ: Summon the servants, Alicia, for I know that Captain Kent has equally favorable news for them. [*Exit* ALICIA.] I'm very grateful to you, Captain Kent, for undertaking so successfully this trading voyage. Tomorrow, I shall go down to the *Unicorn* and direct the unloading of the goods. [SERVANTS *following* ALICIA *have entered during the above conversation and stand listening eagerly.*]

MR. FITZ: I have summoned you to hear from Captain Kent's own lips the result of the undertaking he assumed for all of you. Come, Captain, tell them whether they are richer or poorer by your trading.

CAPTAIN [*Taking small bags from* SAILOR]: In these bags are the rewards you've won from bartering with the people of Barbary. [*Gives one to each—*DICK *gets none.*] In addition, the servants of the royal court sent each of you a small token from their own treasures. [*Hands rolls or packets to all but* DICK.]

MAID [*Examining bag*]: This is more than I'd hoped for, sir.

JOHN: My small offering is more than doubled. I thank you, sir.

MAID: I never thought my woven cloth had such great value. [*Curtseys.*]

COOK: Mr. Fitzwarren spoke aright about the worth of my great green feather. Now, I'll be able to wear two feathers in my new bonnet.

MR. FITZ: Captain Kent appreciates your expressions of gratitude, and I am happy to see you so richly rewarded. And this concludes our business, I presume, Captain?

ALICIA: But what of Dick? Is there nothing for him?

CAPTAIN: Nothing, Miss Alicia [*Teasingly*], nothing but this old box.

[SAILORS *bring large box.*]

MR. FITZ: Now what can the lad do with that?

ALICIA: Heed them not, Dick, I think it's a beautiful box. [*Tries to lift it.*] But Dick, it is so heavy. Open it—hasten—it must be filled with some mysterious surprise.

[DICK *approaches slowly—raises lid and gasps—all gather round him, exclaiming.*]

DICK: But, Captain, this cannot be mine. For what reason do I receive such a gift?

CAPTAIN: It is not a gift, it is your just payment for the merchandise you sent on the *Unicorn*.

DICK: You jest with me, sir. I sent no merchandise. So again I ask you, for what is this payment?

CAPTAIN: It is the price of one small cat.

DICK: But she is just an ordinary cat, not of value to anyone but me.

ALICIA: Father said that Puss would bring success to the voyage.

MR. FITZ: You are a man of great wealth now, Dick, so may I be the first to congratulate you upon your good fortune?

DICK: Sir, all that I have received or have grown to be I owe to you and to Captain Kent. It is my desire that I should share my good fortune with both of you.

MR. FITZ: Nonsense, my lad; both Captain Kent and I are wealthy men. What you have received is yours and yours alone to do with as you wish.

DICK: Then I should like to share with those who work with me. [MR. FITZWARREN *nods affirmatively.*] Here, John, add these coins to those Captain Kent gave you.

JOHN: Thank you, sir. I shall ever remember my association with you.

DICK [*To* MAIDS]: Two strands of golden chain will be yours.

1st MAID: Thank you, oh thank you. In days to come, we will have reason to wear these chains with pride.

DICK [*To* COOK]: What choice is yours, Cook?

COOK [*Whimpering*]: Oh, Master Whittington, I deserve none of your favors. I have often been very hard on you [*changes tone to scolding*] but it was all for your own good! You've been industrious, that's true, but if I hadn't kept you in line, perhaps you'd not have done so well. [*Goes to chest.*] If it is your mind that I should have a part of your treasure— I'll choose this beautiful scarf.

DICK: Certainly, Cook; and with it goes my appreciation for your scoldings and your nagging. I've learned much from you.

MR. FITZ: Now, be off, all of you! [SERVANTS *exit.*] Cook, as a reward for your good fortune, all of you may have a half holiday. But before you go off to celebrate, see that a lunch is placed for us.

COOK: This is wonderful. Thank you, Master; all shall be done as you request. [*Exit.*]

MR. FITZ: Are you not curious, Dick, about the conditions under which you received this great fortune?

DICK: That I am, sir, but I hesitate to ask.

CAPTAIN: Let me tell you. Briefly, here is how it came about. We were received with great honor by the King of Barbary, who had invited us to be his guests while we were in port. Just before the royal feast was to have been served, servants rushed in to the throne room, frightened and crying. They reported that the royal palace was overrun with mice. The King offered great treasure to the one who could get rid of them. So I bartered your cat to chase the mice away. Puss fulfilled all that

I had promised. The King and Queen were so grateful that they both contributed to the chest of gold and jewels which I brought to you.

DICK: I cannot believe that such good luck should come to me! And to think that Puss is responsible for it. How was she, sir, before you left Barbary?

CAPTAIN: She was very happy and content. And she should be, for she has become a great pet of the Queen, who has ordered that she must be the favored one of the court. You need have neither fear nor worry about Puss's future.

DICK: Oh, that is wonderful, sir.

MR. FITZ: During these years that you have spent in my household, Dick, I have watched you with growing interest. You worked faithfully and industriously, never complaining nor asking favors. You have been rewarded most generously. [*Hesitates.*] I have no son to carry on my work, but I will gladly have you work with me. I shall teach you all I know of foreign trade. In time, you will take my place and carry out my plans.

DICK: This is indeed an honor, sir. Your interests and wishes shall always come first with me.

MR. FITZ [*To* CAPTAIN]: Come, Captain, we must turn to our accounting, so that we may pay the crew the wages we've agreed upon. [*To* ALICIA *and* DICK.] Join us soon, and we shall have some refreshment and hear further details of Captain Kent's voyage.

[*Exeunt* MR. FITZWARREN, CAPTAIN *and* SAILORS.]

ALICIA: You are your own master now, Dick. Soon you'll be leaving us to establish your own residence in London.

DICK: But I shall never forget the debt I owe to you and to your father.

ALICIA: To me?

DICK: Yes, to you, for you made it possible for me to keep Puss in my garret. It was you, also, who protected me time and time again from Cook's anger.

ALICIA: We've both been interested in you from the moment you set foot in our house. Now, both of us shall watch with equal interest your progress as a trading master.

DICK: I shall always try to merit the confidence you have in me. I wonder what lies ahead! [*Stops and muses for a moment.*] If you will not laugh at me, I would like to tell you something strange that happened to me before I came to London.

ALICIA: Do tell me, what was it? I shall not laugh.

DICK: You remember the first day I came to your door? Well, I had walked for several days before my arrival and I was tired and discouraged. Twice I decided to turn back and not continue on to London. Then, through the clear air, I heard the evening bells from Bow Church. It seemed to me that they were speaking to me. Over and over again they kept saying, "Keep on, keep on, Whittington, Lord Mayor of London." Well, I did keep on. And now [*pointing to gold*] this has happened! Isn't it strange?

ALICIA [*Breathlessly*]: Lord Mayor of London! Think how grand it will be! [*Bows.*] The Lord Mayor of London rides about the city in a magnificent coach, clad in silken robes, and wearing a golden collar around his neck. [*Takes chain from box, places it around* DICK's *neck.*] No, Dick, it's not so strange as it sounds. Perhaps there *are* even greater honors in store for you. Can't you see the great Abbey filled with people? Gay banners adorn its walls. The trumpet sounds. The King steps down from his throne. You come forward and kneel before him [DICK *kneels.*] and he says [*Taps him on the shoulder.*]: "For all your deeds of bravery and for your loyalty, we dub thee Knight. Arise, Sir Richard!" [*Both laugh.*] Then comes the gay procession—as you ride through the city in your gilded coach—

DICK: But look! Who is that sitting beside me in the coach of state!

ALICIA: Yes, I see someone sitting beside you; but I do not

quite recognize her.

DICK [*Placing coronet from box on her head*]: It's—why, I believe—yes, it must be—*Lady Alicia Whittington!*

ALICIA [*Laughing*]: Why, so it is!

[DICK, *with courtly gesture, bends to kiss her hand. He rises, and taking her hand, leads her grandly from the stage.*]

Curtain

PRODUCTION NOTES

Medieval costumes. Richness of color and material in keeping with the occupation of the characters.

Follow designs in any good medieval costume book or history volume with colored drawings.

Illustrations from the many editions of the story will be suggestive of groupings, scenes, settings and costumes for the play.

BIBLIOGRAPHY

CHILDREN'S THEATER

Burger, Isabel, *Creative Play Acting*. A. S. Barnes & Co., Inc., 1950.

Chorpenning, Charlotte B., *Twenty-one Years with Children's Theatre*. Children's Theatre Press, 1954.

Durland, F. C., *Creative Dramatics for Children*. The Antioch Press, 1952.

Lease, R. G., and Siks, G. B., *Creative Dramatics for Home, School and Community*. Harper, 1952.

Mackay, Constance, *How to Produce Children's Plays*. Henry Holt, 1915.

———, *Children's Theatre and Plays*. Appleton-Century-Crofts, 1927.

Smith, Milton, *Play Production*. Appleton-Century-Crofts, 1948.

Walker, Pamela Prince, *Creative Children's Dramatics*. Hill and Wang, 1957.

Ward, Winifred, *Creative Dramatics*. Appleton-Century-Crofts, 1930.

———, *Play Making with Children*, Revised Edition. Appleton-Century-Crofts, 1957.

———, *Stories to Dramatize*. Children's Theatre Press, 1952.

COSTUMING

Barton, Lucy, *Historic Costumes for the Stage*. Walter H. Baker Co., 1935.

Dabney, Edith, *Book of Dramatic Costumes.* F. S. Crofts & Co., 1930.

Gimbel, E., and Wells, R., *Costuming a Play.* Appleton-Century-Crofts, 1925.

Healy, Daty, *Dress the Show.* Row Peterson & Co., 1948.

Wilcox, R. T., *The Mode in Costume.* Charles Scribner, 1948.

——, *The Mode in Hats and Headdress.* Charles Scribner, 1948.

——, *The Mode in Footwear.* Charles Scribner, 1948.

Young, Agnes, *Stage Costuming.* The Macmillan Co., 1927.

MAKE-UP

Chalmers, Helena, *The Art of Make-Up.* Appleton, 1925.

Corson, Richard, *Stage Make-Up,* Revised Edition. Appleton-Century-Crofts, 1949.

LIGHTING

Selden, Samuel, *Stage Scenery and Lighting,* 3rd Edition. Appleton-Century-Crofts, 1959.

PHYLLIS FENNER

was born in western New York State, educated at Mount Holyoke College and Columbia University's School of Library Service. After trying social work, department-store work and teaching, she "fell into" library work quite by accident. For a long time, she says, she felt guilty about being paid for doing anything so rewarding and such fun. For thirty-two years she was librarian at the Plandome Road School in Manhasset, Long Island, New York. For seven years she taught story telling and children's literature summers and Saturdays at St. John's University, Brooklyn.

Retiring to Manchester, Vermont, in 1955, to write and travel, Miss Fenner found another joy in gardening. Book reviewing, writing about children's reading and books and making anthologies of stories for young people more than fill her days. She has over thirty books to her credit.

AVAH HUGHES

was a member of the staff of Lincoln School, Teachers College, Columbia University, for twenty-one years. When the school was terminated, she went to the public schools of Manhasset, New York, where she has been teaching for the past thirteen years.

She has given courses in children's literature, creative language and reading at the University of California at Los Angeles; the University of North Carolina; Teachers College, Columbia University and elsewhere.

She has had extensive experience in writing and editing materials for children in the middle grades, including work for E. M. Hale and Company, the *Young America Reader, Young America* magazines and *Scholastic* magazines.

A native of Kentucky, she now lives in Great Neck, Long Island, and teaches a sixth grade at the Plandome Road School, Manhasset.